silent night

HOLY WAR

The Epic Story of Jesus' Birth as Never Before Told

RON SUSEK

Susek Evangelistic Association
P.O. Box 3007, Gettysburg, PA 17325
Phone: (717) 337-1170 Fax: (717) 337-1833
E-mail: RonSusek@aol.com
www.silentnightholywar.com

Susek Evangelistic Association
P.O. Box 3007, Gettysburg, PA 17325
Phone: (717) 337-1170 Fax: (717) 337-1833
E-mail: RonSusek@aol.com
www.silentnightholywar.com

Golden ✒ Quill
P U B L I S H I N G
Gettysburg, Pennsylvania

© 2006 by Ron Susek

First Printing, September 2006

Printed in the United States of America

Library of Congress
ISBN 978-0-9789727-0-7
0-978-9727-0-8

Dedicated to
The One whose victory at birth
proved His name -
Immanuel (God With Us)

To
Kelly & Adam
my new Friends

Rom. 8:28-29

The Birth of This Book

While reading Revelation 12, I made a shocking discovery about the night Christ was born: On that night, one of the most violent wars between the powers of light and the powers of darkness took place. This discovery has forever changed my view and appreciation of Christ's birth. Let me give you some background.

For me, there was always something lacking in the traditional way we as Christians recognize the birth of Christ. Certainly it was not the true meaning of the season or the celebration of it: grand music, festive events, gifts, goodwill. It wasn't easy to put my finger on the cause of my discontent.

Then, one recent Christmas, while reading a passage in Revelation 12, where Jesus took John back to the night of his birth and showed him what had been seen by the eyes of heaven, I finally grasped what was missing: the real-life tension, the deadly drama, the clash of two worlds that occurred during Christ's birth. In so doing, God graciously answered a prayer that was more like an empty longing than a conscious thought, and, from that point on, Christmas has become a profoundly meaningful experience.

As I studied the Revelation 12 text, I realized that the Church had slowly, down through the centuries, sacrificed fact for frosting. We had made the story so saccharine that many people tended to treat the Christmas story as a bedtime tale, instead of an historic event that warrants our commitment.

Let me elaborate: We basically have had Mary, who was nine months pregnant, riding a donkey over eighty miles and arriving in Bethlehem with a sweet disposition, then experiencing a painless birth amid smiling angels. The worst thing that happened was that Mary and Joseph couldn't get a room in the inn at Bethlehem, so they got bumped to a shepherds' cave. That provided a slight tug on the heartstrings but nothing too suspenseful or dangerous; after all, throughout the centuries millions of children have been born in undesirable places.

So what's wrong with the Christmas story, as we have known it, being tension-free and tranquil? The most serious problem is that we have not thoroughly represented the biblical account. We lifted the facts out of the Gospels but missed the passage in Revelation.

The ominous events that rumbled in the invisible realms would not be known to the world if Jesus had not revealed them to John the Apostle nearly a century after the Lord's birth. It was after Christ's death and resurrection that he raised John up in the spirit from his dank prison cell on the Isle of Patmos to heaven's throne room. At that time Jesus showed John the end of the world. Amid those revelations, John was also taken back to the night of Christ's birth. There he saw the violent clash between the kingdoms of light and darkness that occurred.

While not all of John's imagery in the book of Revelation can be fully understood, still the applications are always literal. The story in this book is based largely on the Revelation 12 account. Here we discover a breathtaking drama, filled with tension equal to that of Christ's death and resurrection. The true story shows Immanuel ("God with us") stepping onto our planet, in the fullness of time, in infant form amid one of the greatest spiritual wars of all time. It awakens our awareness to a helpless child coming in victory over the powers of hell, but not without a flood of danger. It is in this fuller understanding of the story that we learn the depth to which God stooped to lift us up.

One word of explanation must be given. Not every scene or character in this story is found in the Bible—but they are all possible. The only inerrant account of the people and events is that found in the Bible. This story is designed to take the skeletal form of revealed truth and dress it with the flesh and blood, the sweat and callus, the villain and victor of real life.

Another minor word of warning must be given: Readers may feel disquieted over Jesus being born in a cave and not a stable. The fact is that stables did not exist at that time. If you are among the millions of people who have been privileged to visit the Holy Land, you will recall that there are two sites that could have been the birthplace of Christ. Both are caves—shepherds' caves. So, in this story, Jesus will be born as it was—in a cave.

I have several hopes for this book: One, that you will return to the Bible, read it, and understand it more fully. In light of this, I have footnoted Bible references so that, after you read the story, you can conduct a careful study.

Two, that by enlarging the story of Christ's birth, Christmas will be exalted above "Seasons Greetings" to a reality, demanding life-changing devotion.

Three, that new levels of authentic worship will be lifted up on high and warm the heart of God.

I am confident that the angels who appeared to the shepherds on the slopes just outside of Bethlehem will gladly make room for you and me to join them in saying, "Glory to God in the highest, and on earth peace to men on whom his favor rests" (Luke 2:14).

A great and wondrous sign appeared in heaven: a woman clothed with the sun, with the moon under her feet and a crown of twelve stars on her head. She was pregnant and cried out in pain as she was about to give birth. Then another sign appeared in heaven: an enormous red dragon with seven heads and ten horns and seven crowns on his heads. His tail swept a third of the stars out of the sky and flung them to the earth. The dragon stood in front of the woman who was about to give birth, so that he might devour her child the moment it was born. She gave birth to a son, a male child, who will rule all the nations with an iron scepter.

Revelation 12:1-5a

CHAPTER ONE

Gabriel, Go Now

"The fullness of time has come. Go now!"

This long-awaited directive flowed from God's throne to Gabriel, that magnificent, quiet-hearted warrior angel, who historically has been God's primary messenger to bear divine words to the people of Earth. Gabriel rose from kneeling on the crystal clear sea of glass encircling God's throne and sheathed his sword that had been honorably pointed downward. Since his creation, Gabriel never lost his sense of reverence when summoned to the throne.

He had just been commissioned to take the grandest Word since creation to a young girl in Nazareth. Cascading banks of angels surrounding the throne gasped in amazement, though none could fully comprehend the magnitude of events about to unfold. A holy, silent worship swept through the gathering.

Earth bore a different scene: an unseen creature pacing, his entire being trembling. Satan's panic would be pitiful except that his putrid wound was self-inflicted while swinging the sword of rebellion against God. Bitterness has oozed from the gash, infecting all whom he touches ever since.

Satan never knew when this moment would arrive, the moment when the Messiah would come to crush his head and destroy his reign. He was sure, however, that God would someday invade his kingdom to destroy his vile works—on the very planet where he had drawn mankind into rebellion. True to form, he prepared to fight Immanuel upon his arrival, clinging vainly to the hope that this time he might win.

He had often flexed his muscles through the ages trying to forestall, even stop God before this showdown. He inspired the murder of prophets who predicted the coming Savior. He encouraged Israel's love affair with pagan beliefs and practices and rejoiced when Israel hardened her heart toward God. He delighted when divine rebuke fell upon both Israel and the surrounding nations.

Knowing from prophecy that God would come as an infant, Satan harbored a fiendish hope that he might prevail. He also knew that he was running out of time, and opportunities to continue his futile madness to either dethrone God or derail his plan were few.

On this night, far to the east, eyes scanned back and forth across the dark skies in search of a message from God. Many had long practiced this tradition born from a belief in the coming of the Messiah. While it was known that the Messiah would come through the Jews, many proselytes awaited, even sought his arrival. (Proselytes were the faithful Gentiles who often displayed greater devotion to God than many of the chosen.)

Such were the Magi who spent long nights diligently observing the heavens to see if the time had come. Their faithfulness delighted God, who had determined to give them a sign among the constellations. But this seemed like just another night, one like the hundreds before it. Stars . . . just stars. No message yet.

It was an odd Jewish pair—not married to each other—who fascinated many in the temple at Jerusalem. The one called Anna had lived in the temple for decades, devoting herself to fasting and prayer. The other, Simeon, came and went each day, entreating God hour after hour. The intensity of their purpose made the priests appear derelict in contrast. They pled with God to send the One whom the prophets foretold and the Magi sought.

Respected by the priests, revered by the godly, mocked by children and hated by Satan, Anna and Simeon daily approached God's throne to pray. They were unaware of the command given this day to Gabriel on high; however they noticed a new heaviness falling upon their spirits, drawing them deeper into prayer. They faithfully persisted, not knowing what the urgency meant.

For several months an intriguing story had spread like wildfire from a village somewhere in the hills of Judea, not far from Jerusalem. People talked about it with mixed belief. An unearthly messenger had visited the elderly priest Zechariah, bearing remarkable news. Since that mysterious encounter, Zechariah and his wife Elizabeth knew that the Messiah was soon to come, though they knew not where or when. Somehow, they just knew.

Nazareth was a small village nestled in the craggy hills of Galilee. Here lived a simple but devoted family: a mother, father and a daughter known as Mary who was betrothed to a man named Joseph. There was not a whisper of a hint this day that the Word given to Gabriel would soon thrust this couple into the flash point of another great contest between God and the devil.

On high, Gabriel stepped back from God's throne, raised his head and looked directly at his Master. There sat God the Father, Son and Holy Spirit—glorious, powerful, resolute. He saw not form, but rather a holy brilliance radiating from the throne. Lightning bolts flashed and thunder rolled as the Word was given—a Word determined before the foundations of the world. The time of redemption had come. Gabriel was about to announce the coming of the Messiah to Mary and, furthermore, that the anointed One would be born into the world through her.

The mighty angel saw an unoccupied throne at God's right hand. He caught his breath as he thought, *This is the very throne upon which the Son will be seated to reign over his redeemed creation.* He was overwhelmed by what he saw: Salvation's plan was drawing nigh.

He scanned the endless sea of glass flowing outward from the Father's throne. It was an extravagant sight, sparkling as clear as crystal. He had seen it many times before and sensed it was readied for a great event. Now it came together in his mind: *This is where the vast throng of the redeemed will come to flood the eternal One with worship and praise.* His throat choked with uncontainable joy.

Gabriel adjusted his sword, knowing the fury that would confront him upon entering the constellations. His assignment would not be easy. Earth, though mystically draped in a bluish veil, was also wrapped in spiritual darkness—the result of Adam's fall. And the darkness was enforced by evil powers. He knew these dark forces would be poised for resistance—for war.

Despite the danger, Gabriel rejoiced. Redemption time had come. He felt the immediacy of God's words, "Go now!" resounding in his being like the cadence of a march.

The majestic commander, fully arrayed in divine authority, departed the throne with the snap of obedience; his eyes turned toward earth. As heaven's glorious glow receded, thoughts flooded Gabriel's mind.

Why now? he wondered. *Why is this the fullness of time?* It did not appear to be a good time on earth for the Savior to come.

The Roman Empire was at the zenith of its five-hundred-year climb to power, gripping the Mediterranean world by raw muscle. The dripping blood from Roman swords never dried from the massacre of rivals and royalties alike. Caesar Augustus, the current emperor of Rome, came to power after his uncle Julius Caesar's assassination, followed by blood-soaked battles with other contenders for the throne.

The Roman Empire honored gods whom they believed enhanced and protected their achievements. The powers of Rome, then, would surely degrade the idea of a messiah as being no more than the fanciful dream of the conquered Jews—a vain hope in the midst of their defeat.

In addition, since the Jews were powerless subjects of Rome, they suffered under the infamous Gentile king Herod the Great who reigned over Jerusalem. Herod answered to Caesar Augustus in Rome and had a thirst for power that was robbing his sanity, leaving him deranged enough to attempt the murder of any would-be king of the Jews. He had become a willing dupe for the father of all murder.

Gabriel also knew that God's people had drifted far from the revelations given to her prophets. The majority of the Jews looked for a messiah who would overthrow Rome and establish them as the world's superpower, but they were not seeking a redeemer to save them from their sins; after all, many were convinced they could save themselves by keeping the Ten Commandments, plus numerous man-made rules added by the Pharisees. Gabriel was saddened to think that Abraham's descendants were no closer to God than when Jeremiah wrote, "But these people have stubborn and rebellious hearts; they have turned aside and gone away."[1]

The scene on earth was clearly to Satan's advantage. If ever he had a chance to defeat God it would be now. There was nothing to support God's purpose except his own strong arm. *What a perfect time for God to demonstrate his all-sufficient power,* thought Gabriel.

So, it was clear that earthly events were not guiding God's decision to send Gabriel now. Gabriel knew that his message would set an all-out war in motion. There must be a deeper reason. With that, Gabriel descended toward earth, his thoughts immersed in greater contemplation.

He reflected upon God's sovereign right to do anything he wants anytime he chooses. But he knew that God never did things out of ruthless arrogance, only pure love. He knew how deeply God loved this highest of all creation and how deeply his heart ached over Adam's fall. And he knew of the promises God had made to the faithful remnant who sought him in each generation. God's ultimate promise was about to be fulfilled; the Redeemer was coming!

As the mighty angel saw earth's glow he reflected upon the severe twenty-one day battle he encountered with powers of darkness when taking an end-time prophecy to Daniel.[2] That struggle was so fierce, it demanded the help of Michael the archangel. If the message to Daniel had met with such opposition, then this one would undoubtedly be greater, since God was about to enter the world through a virgin to save all of creation and break Satan's grip—forever!

Gabriel pictured God as an infant and thought, *If ever the evil one would try to overthrow God, it would indeed be now.* Certain that the world would be plunged into a great spiritual war, Gabriel knew he was bringing both a decree of birth and a declaration of battle.

Suddenly, Gabriel burst out of eternity and into time, out of infinity and into space, out of heaven and into the cosmos. He always thrilled to see creation displayed in panoramic view: constellations clustered throughout the darkness, mystically thick, like vast, haunting patches of fog; planets gliding like mute behemoths on invisible strings of gravity; suns bursting with violent beauty, sending light and energy into the deep silence.

Gabriel crossed light years in seconds, racing toward earth.

As he traveled, he passed a blazing star rushing toward earth as though shot from a bow. Soon it would come into view of the Magi in the east who were searching the skies for a message from God.

Approaching earth's solar system, Gabriel saw powers of darkness flurry like disturbed flies. Troubled to see mighty Gabriel approaching, they scurried to inform Satan. Drawing his sword, Gabriel broke into earth's gravitational ring and descended until he hovered over Nazareth, his eyes eventually lighting upon the young girl named Mary. Then, he immediately began to prepare the right setting for the announcement: his short and poignant Word from God.

Gabriel looked upon Mary, who was beginning her day, and marveled at God's plan. The girl appeared so carefree. Gabriel knew that she must be a young woman of noble character for God's favor to fall upon her. But she had choice of will. She could reject the divine edict. Should she accept the commission, the messenger knew she would face a responsibility far beyond her natural strength. She would be subject to direct conflict with Satan, much suffering and grief, severe rejection and pain. But then, too, she would be the one through whom God's salvation would enter the world. Indeed, she would be saying yes to the most extraordinary opportunity of any woman before or after her.

Gabriel finished arranging for the encounter to occur in a place of open isolation. He waited for Mary at the village well.

[1]Jeremiah 5:23
[2]Daniel 10:13

CHAPTER TWO

One Bright Day in Nazareth

It's hard to imagine that the greatest event since creation was about to fall upon a plain girl, and on such a typical day in her obscure village. The sun rose, giving no hint of Gabriel's presence. It simply lit the stage for Scene One of the drama—the annunciation—that was about to change the course of world history.

An easterly wind blew enchanting warmth from the desert, and floral fragrance scented the air. The heart of Nazareth snuggled deeply in the center of a circular formation of mountains, west of the Sea of Galilee. One crevice in the eastern side provided a view of the Valley of Jezreel.

Mary lived with her family in a small sandstone house, its roof and floor made of baked clay. It was perched high on the steep western slope of Nazareth, and the scene from Mary's home was vast. One could look down upon the housetops below, or out through the crevice and across the valley to the mountains beyond.

On this morning the sun was diffused by the morning mist rising from the valley, giving the mystical illusion of a never-ending land. Mary stood barefoot on the small doorstep, invigorated by the cool clay. She stretched her arms high to catch the gentle breeze that caused her gown to caress her skin. She had no earthshaking plans or desires, but simply felt intoxicated with life itself.

Mary was still too young and sheltered for life's harshness to have corroded her soul. Her youthful mind was not yet cluttered by the complexities or inevitable storms of life: setbacks, denials, rejections, betrayals, injustices and losses. Her faith was still unrestricted.

Then, too, there was Joseph. While her soon-coming marriage had been arranged by the couple's parents, she was in love with the man of their choice. This love brought greater mystery and intrigue to her than the lure of the misty valley beyond the mountain.

Mary turned her light, olive-toned face toward the rising sun and smiled. Her dark eyebrows gracefully arched above her fawn-like, gentle eyes; transparent eyes through which her emotions freely flowed: joy, sorrow, compassion, fear, anger. She couldn't hide her heart. Her eyes *always* revealed her soul.

Her nose was pronounced, but attractive. Her long, raven hair was straight and shiny. Her lips were sharply etched against her tanned complexion. A dainty, yet firm chin exhibited something of the strong character residing within her. Mary was wholesome both in appearance and demeanor. She would shyly tilt her head downward when talking with people, suggesting naivety, even vulnerability. But she bore rock-hard integrity, gritty tenacity and wisdom beyond her years.

From the center of town she heard the dull thud of a wooden mallet rhythmically banging against a chisel. It was Joseph—*her* Joseph—carving a beautiful door that would adorn their home after the wedding. The sound stirred like a nightingale's song. She held her breath hoping to capture the feeling forever. She felt as though she could stop breathing and yet live on. Anything seemed possible because she was in love, in love with a man whose integrity won unquestioned respect throughout Nazareth. Everyone knew that his workmanship surpassed his price. He didn't just make things, he crafted beauty. More than a carpenter, he was an artist. And he loved Mary too. She thought about soon waking in their own home.

She caught herself humming.

Mary was a simple girl in love with a simple man—both approaching life with uncluttered hearts. They held scriptural truth to be absolute, not debating it as though wiser than God. Ostentatious ambitions were foreign to them. They cared only for life's basics: their love, a home, children and God. They frequented the synagogue, setting their moral boundaries by the Law of Moses and learning all they could about God's Word. Joseph enjoyed the stories of King David's exploits, though he related more in temperament to Jonathan—David's loyal friend who willingly played a subordinate role, gladly surrendering his throne-right to David. Mary was particularly drawn to Abigail, whose wise counsel aided David in his ascent to the throne.

But there were emotional moments in the synagogue that Mary didn't understand. It seemed like a grand, mysterious message was trying to enter her heart—a premonition. It would occur when someone read the words, "For to us a child is born, to us a son is given, and the government will be on his shoulders. And he will be called Wonderful Counselor, Mighty God, Everlasting Father, Prince of Peace."[1] The passage lodged deep within her soul, as if calling to her as a participant. But of course she never spoke of it, not to anyone.

Still, the haunting mystery deepened each time a rabbi read, "Therefore the Lord himself will give you a sign: The virgin will be with child and will give birth to a son, and will call him Immanuel."[2] She'd feel the loving ownership of a mother stir within, but modesty would not permit her to pursue the impression. Every Jew anticipated that a chosen woman would someday birth the Messiah, but surely this would be a prominent Jewess in Jerusalem, perhaps the daughter of the high priest, certainly not a plain girl in Nazareth. Thus, Mary suppressed her impressions, resting in the thought that all young girls must have such feelings. To be certain never to face ridicule, she hid the thoughts and feelings in the privacy of her heart.

On this morning, however, she was thinking of none of these things. She was drinking in the freshness of life and stirred by the anticipation of marrying Joseph. The rising sun nudged her toward the daily chores. She yawned, rubbed her cheeks, spun back into the house and put on a brown, woolen robe and tied a cord around her waist.

It was time to go to the village well for water. The only unusual thing about this day was that her friends didn't gather, as they usually did, to walk together. They normally talked and laughed about light things and, of course, always about Joseph. Wondering what could have hindered them, she started down the mountain alone.

Mary loved living high on the mountainside but dreaded the steep climb bearing a jar of water. The secret was to walk slowly taking short steps. Her poetic nature caused her to ponder how life is like the mountain: sometimes a fun, easy descent with an empty jar; at other times a burdensome uphill climb with a full jar. The whisper of a voice seemed to brush her soul saying, *This is preparation, Mary . . . this is preparation.* It could have been easily missed, much like a quiet breeze. She didn't linger on the thought.

With a contagious smile, she greeted everyone along her way, briefly relieving life's burdens from many hearts. Her innocent spring-of-step awakened in people the desire to start anew. While she was loved by all, no one saw her rising in stature beyond the village, and certainly not beyond the world. She was just a common girl who brought delight to the drudgery of village routine.

Mary's clear skin glistened like bronze in the sunlight, adding to her vibrancy. She was delicate in structure, but strong in muscle. Like a graceful dancer, her feet glided softly, leaving little imprint on the switchback path. Each sharp turn was a steep drop, demanding careful step.

Mary was surprised to find no one at the well—a strange thing for mid-morning. Lowering her brown clay jar into the cool, rushing water, she lay on the ground and stretched her arm down into the well to dangle her fingers in the current. It felt smooth and clean. She lifted the jar from the stream and sat it on the ground, preparing to hoist it upon her head.

That's when it happened. Without warning or preparation, the unseen world exploded before her eyes, and a form materialized from nowhere. Frightened, Mary drew back trembling. Gabriel, the mighty angel who appears only for cosmic events, scanned the mountaintops to let the chattering imps of hell know not to come near, then spoke: "Greetings, you who are highly favored! The Lord is with you."[3] His voice sounded richer than human, with command and compassion intoning and flowing as one.

Mary knit her brows in contemplation. Questions raced through her mind: *What could this greeting mean? Is this an eccentric person? A crazy person? Could this actually be an angel?*

He continued:

> Do not be afraid, Mary, you have found favor with God. You will be with child and give birth to a son, and you are to give him the name Jesus. He will be great and will be called the Son of the Most High. The Lord God will give him the throne of his father David, and he will reign over the house of Jacob forever; his kingdom will never end.[4]

In her thin, youthful voice, Mary asked the angel, "How will this be, since I am a virgin?" She felt startled by her strength to speak clearly.

The angel answered, "The Holy Spirit will come upon you, and the power of the Most High will overshadow you. So the holy one to be born will be called the Son of God."[5]

Mary was not in a trance, but was oblivious of the world around her. She was transported to the ethereal, while still in the natural realm. Enraptured, she gazed upon the angel, who continued with the extraordinary announcement: "Even Elizabeth your relative is going to have a child in her old age, and she who was said to be barren is in her sixth month. For nothing is impossible with God."[6]

Mary's response showed maturity beyond her years: "I am the Lord's servant. May it be to me as you have said."[7]

Gabriel departed, and the angelic moment passed. It had started suddenly, lasted briefly and ended abruptly. Mary was alone again, clutching his words close to her heart—transfixed in thought. She stood motionless, fossilized by the experience. Someone from the unseen world had just appeared to her and now was gone. In that moment this unsuspecting girl became a key player in the historic unfolding of God's plan to redeem a people for himself. There was no rehearsal for this event. This was real life, not a play. Mary had just been thrust into the highest privilege ever to be bestowed upon a woman. Centuries of Jewish prayers and yearning for the Messiah were about to come to fruition through her.

A million shifting eyes peered over the rim above Nazareth. Frantically, the demons muttered powerlessly while watching the event unfold. Though they hated Gabriel, none dared attack him. He was too powerful. Nor could they attack Mary, as she was surrounded by a heavenly guard. The ruling principality of darkness rushed to Pergamum, where Satan had his throne,[8] to inform him of the event. Horror reigned.

Needing to gather her strength, Mary sat down and leaned her arm across the jar of water. Life as she had known it was starting again, though slowly, and she didn't feel ready for it. She saw a palm tree swaying lazily by the well, heard birds chirping and singing. Behind her an old man was leading a donkey laden with bundles of vegetables destined for the market. While the world seemed normal again, she was still traversing the gulf between the seen and the unseen worlds. She had just been visited by Gabriel. He brought this awesome message straight from God. She was told that she had been chosen by God to mother the long-awaited Messiah. Mary felt faint.

"Favored?" she whispered, unaware she was speaking out loud. "I am 'highly favored'? I have been chosen to bring the Messiah into the world?" She was trying to adjust to and absorb the message. The ultimate dream of every Hebrew virgin had just come to her—she was the chosen one.

She rubbed her arms and face, as though dispelling numbness, and hoped no one would come near; she wouldn't know what to say. Life had become surreal, yet it had actually happened—Gabriel had actually appeared.

Why do I feel so weak? she wondered. To her mind came the memories of men like Daniel, who upon seeing an angel fell down as dead. It was her awe of holy things, her surprise of peering into the unseen, her amazement to be chosen by God that made her weak. And there was no one who could help her, since no one else had ever been here before, or ever would again.

Finally, in an effort to collect her wits, she gave herself audible instructions. "All right, life is going on—so must I. The first thing I must do is carry this water up the hill. Yes, that's it, I must carry the water up the hill. That's the first thing. Come on, Mary, carry the water."

At last she stood up, straightened her clothes and brushed dust from her robe. She looked around, wondering if anyone was watching her. The man leading the donkey was gone. She saw no one, and felt relieved. Still a simple virgin—just an earthborn girl—she hoisted the jar of water to her head and started the mundane walk up the mountain to her home. In every way the day was the same as it had been, but her life was now forever changed.

Many questions coursed through her mind as she ascended the hill.

"Why did God choose me?" she mumbled aloud. She had an inward, pure beauty but wasn't striking in appearance. She was chaste but not beyond many others. What caused her to find favor—special favor—with God?

"I'm just a sinner like everyone else. How can I, a sinner, bear the sinless One?" Realizing that these questions were too vast for her to answer, she said, "I'll wait and ask Abba, he'll know."

She simply rested in that. She would ask her father.

It was helpful that Mary's mind was richly filled with the Scriptures. While her family had few earthly possessions, they were wealthy in spiritual heritage. As a child Mary memorized large portions of the Psalms and Proverbs. Long evenings were spent at home discussing Moses' law and the ebb and flow of Israel's historic relationship with God. Her father told stories of the kings, always highlighting David—always. Her mother and father brought biblical truths and stories to life.

Now, she needed every drop of that background to enable her to handle the enormous weight of the announcement that had just entered her life. Mary continued to climb and talk softly to herself, still trying to sort everything out.

"I have always wanted to please you, God, but I never expected anything special from you. I simply anticipated being married to Joseph, cooking, drawing water, raising our children, that's all." Mary was devoted to this carpenter named Joseph, who, in turn, was devoted to his Mary. Until now, life was that simple.

She had held the flower of her youth in sacred reserve for the man of God's choosing—she was a virgin. She had devoted herself to Jehovah God while living in the nondescript village of Nazareth, a village mocked as incompetent to produce anything good. Perhaps that's partly why God chose to bring the Christ out of Nazareth, a place representing the world's outcast.

Mary, the simple girl clad in a plain robe, climbed the hill. On her head was water that could not quench thirst forever. In her womb was conceived the Living Water who could.

The morning drew late. Shadows shortened. Preoccupied in thought, she responded to people's greetings, but they seemed distant. The jar of water felt light. A new question surfaced, a pressing and immediate question: *How will I explain this to Joseph?*

Mary reached home and placed the jar of water in the courtyard. She methodically completed the rest of her daily chores, but the swirling questions consumed her thoughts. With her work completed, she sat staring beyond the Valley of Jezreel and into eternity. It was all too grand to comprehend.

Her parents noticed that she was drawn deep within herself at the evening meal. Honoring her privacy they asked no questions. Later, she sat alone outside, feeling both excited and afraid, still wondering: *How will Joseph react? Will he believe my story?*

When the moon was high in the sky and the stars were clustered as thick as smoke, Mary went to bed.

[1]Isaiah 9:6
[2]Isaiah 7:14
[3]Luke 1:28
[4]Luke 1:30-33
[5]Luke 1:35
[6]Luke 1:36-37
[7]Luke 1:38
[8]Revelation 2:13

CHAPTER THREE

One Dark Day in Nazareth

Mary awakened early the next morning feeling the same, just as human as ever. A wind from the east was blowing another mild day across Nazareth. She tossed her blankets back to feel the air dance gently on her skin. It was fresh and sweet. She lay perfectly still, wondering how she had found favor with God, knowing she was no better than a thousand others—a question she was determined to ask her Abba. She pictured the angel in her mind and recounted his words exactly, even saying them aloud, pausing after each phrase in order to etch them into the granite of her memory.

Do not be afraid, Mary, you have found favor with God. You will be with child and give birth to a son, and you are to give him the name Jesus. He will be great and will be called the Son of the Most High. The Lord God will give him the throne of his father David, and he will reign over the house of Jacob forever; his kingdom will never end. The Holy Spirit will come upon you, and the power of the Most High will overshadow you. So the holy one to be born will be called the Son of God.[1]

She crisscrossed her arms under her head, reflecting upon what had happened only one day before. She had met Gabriel! His presence was brief but lasting, frightening but safe. No words were wasted. He was on a mission from the Almighty. And Mary, young Mary, was suddenly exalted to a lofty responsibility. She was jolted from youthful frivolity to a divine call that would demand the maturity of a sage. But her mind was not filled with counting the cost so much as embracing the blessing.

She was quiet again at breakfast. Her parents concluded that her mood wasn't from a tiff with Joseph, since her spirit was warm and pleasant, just withdrawn.

After breakfast Mary put on a long, white dress—Joseph's favorite. The dress intensified her dark complexion. It puffed over her shoulders and hung loosely down to mid-calf. She wrapped a long white sash around her waist, tied her brown leather sandals and descended the hill, turning onto the path leading to Joseph's shop. The familiar thick sound of a mallet pounding against a chisel grew louder as she drew near. Her steps quickened as she thought of her beloved.

Joseph's well-defined arms and shoulders resulted from his trade. His hair was jet black and hung to the bottom of his neck. His beard was full but neatly trimmed. Along with deep-set eyes, strong cheekbones and a firm, square jaw, he had the build and agility of an athlete, but the spirit of a dove. His muscular appearance provoked respect, but his gentle heart solicited trust. Above all, he was esteemed for his moral code. He was a virtuous man, solid in character.

Joseph was carving an ornate door for his Mary, a door for their new home. He dreamed of the statement of love this would be for all to see, carved with sheep, birds and vines with clusters of grapes.

Unexpectedly, a shadow fell across his work. He looked up. Mary was standing in the doorway.

"Mary!" He intoned with delight.

She entered softly. "I must share something with you,

Joseph, that will not be easy to explain. But you must believe me. You must believe every word of it." Her voice was firm with conviction, her eyes were leveled directly at his.

"Of course, my love, you know I'll believe you."

"Joseph, yesterday when I went to the well for water, I was alone. My friends didn't join me as usual, and strangely, no one else was at the well. After drawing the water, I sat the jar on the ground. Before lifting it to my head, someone spoke to me. I turned in surprise, since no one had been near, and . . . and . . . oh, Joseph, you must promise to believe me." Her voice trembled with joy.

"You know I will, Mary." He took hold of her shoulders, his attention undivided.

"Joseph, it was Gabriel, Gabriel!" Joseph slightly cocked his head to the side, still looking into her eyes. "Please, I'm not jesting, nor did I simply imagine it. Gabriel the archangel appeared to me!"

Time froze. Joseph studied her. There was no hint of lightheartedness. She was excited, but dead serious.

"What did he say?" Joseph asked in a faint whisper, as a torrent of questions flooded his mind.

"I'm going to give you his exact words. They are forever imbedded in my mind. He said, 'Greetings, you who are highly favored! The Lord is with you.'"[2]

Joseph lowered his hands from her shoulders, backed away a few steps and leaned against their door that lay on the worktable in the middle of his shop.

"Joseph, I thought it was a dream at first, but slowly his presence became more real than the trees around me. He went on to say, 'Do not be afraid, Mary, you have found favor with God. You will be with child and give birth to a son, and you are to give him the name Jesus. He will be great and will be called the Son of the Most High. The Lord God will give him the throne of his father David, and he will reign over the house of Jacob forever; his kingdom will never end.'[3]

"I asked him, Joseph, how this could be, since I am a virgin, and Gabriel answered, 'The Holy Spirit will come upon you, and the power of the Most High will overshadow you. So the holy one to be born will be called the Son of God.'"[4]

Mary's eyes pled for Joseph's acceptance of her story. At first his eyes glistened with favor.

"Mary, are you saying that you have been chosen to mother the Messiah?"

"Yes. That's the only thing it could mean."

The wall of choice stood directly in front of Joseph. He was forced to choose between believing Mary or the questions—those dark, ominous questions gathering like a storm in his mind. He clutched his head as weightless thought became like tonnage upon his soul.

Then, after a lengthy pause, Joseph snapped his head to one side. His voice resounded like a thunderclap, "No! . . . No!" His heart told him he had been betrayed, that she had been with another man and now dared to concoct this story so he would raise the child. This way she would not suffer disgrace in the village. All would think the child was Joseph's, especially if they married immediately. Perhaps she wanted only to ensure not being stoned to death, as that ancient law was still in pharisaical hearts.

Joseph turned to face the wall, took a few steps away from Mary, then, enlarged with anger, he turned back and fixed his eyes on hers. Steeped in legalistic training, he was intolerant of moral failure. He was a *righteous* man! She didn't fear his hand, but was frightened by his heart. A volcano of molten rage erupted from deep within his being, so forceful that it surprised even himself.

"How dare you say these words, Mary!" Addressing her as though she were an unknown enemy—an object!—his voice heavy with condemnation. His robe swayed from his sudden turn. He raised his finger toward Jehovah, then pointed it toward her, intending to impale her with guilt. She drew back shocked, pitiful, confused. He yelled in hot, breathy tones so that others would not hear. "It's one thing to have been unfaithful, but it's altogether another matter to lie, claiming to have conceived the Messiah by the Holy Spirit. This is a double sin—blasphemy!"

Stone cold silence reigned as he slowly lowered his finger, his body quaking from the shock of this sudden outburst.

Mary quivered. She only had strength left to whisper, "You don't believe me, Joseph. You don't believe me. You think I betrayed you. Made up a lie." Her voice sounded pathetic, like that of a wounded animal. Her eyes rimmed with tears soon to burst through her strength.

"Joseph?" she said in a questioning tone to test his response. He looked at the floor as though staring into hell. She removed all question from her tone and spoke more directly, though her voice was soft and pleading, "Joseph. Look at me." As she reached up to turn his face toward hers, he snapped his head and drove his stare deeper into the ground. More than Joseph's pride was at stake; his belief system was shaken as well. All his life he believed that God would never let the righteous fall. But now, his whole world appeared to be collapsing around his feet.

"Joseph. Look at me." Her voice thickened with sternness, insisting that he listen. "These may be my final words to you in this life."

He slowly looked up, leveling an expression of contempt directly into her eyes.

"Joseph, I have not lied. I can only pray that God will reveal this truth to you. I do love you and have been faithful to you. There is no other."

She buried her face in her hands, turned and rushed away. Joseph stared into emptiness as her delicate form disappeared through the doorway. He had no thoughts, just a boiling heart. Turning slowly, he bent over and picked up the only friends he had left: a hammer and chisel. Just as Mary's emotions were expressed through her eyes, so Joseph's were expressed through his hands. He instinctively tried to resume etching the ornate door, but his hands shook. The mallet seemed unbearably heavy. Joseph felt weaker than water poured out on the ground.

As he tapped lightly, his mind rummaged through imaginations of whom Mary may have been with. No one. He couldn't think of a single person. Still, he was certain that this conception was not a divine miracle. The thought of her story brought a bitter taste to his mouth. He spit, but the brackish taste remained dark and thick like tar.

Concentration was impossible. His mind was freefalling into a bottomless pit of despair. He felt nauseous, and dark spots danced dizzily before his eyes.

From someplace within his thoughts came a hot, belittling voice taunting, *Fool . . . you fool! You're nothing but a carpenter. She was enamored with someone of wealth and power. She's gone. You're alone, you worthless fool. What made you think she'd be happy with your little world?*

The inanimate door he had been carving for Mary took on a life of its own, mocking his tender devotion to her, confirming him to be a fool.

He swung the hammer heavily against the chisel, shattering an entire cluster of wooden grapes. One violent swing followed another until destruction gripped the helm of his heart. Somehow he had to cut his love for Mary out of his heart, but his attempt to destroy it only added to the throbbing pain within. No matter what he did, he couldn't remove the love or stop the pain.

He hit the chisel harder and harder, splintering the ornate carvings across the room. He whirled and groaned in madness, gouging deeper and deeper until ghastly grooves scarred the door. Spit flew onto his beard. His lean, powerful muscles pulsated with raging strength, as faster and faster he mindlessly bashed the door.

Wishing he could die, he chiseled his emotions in the door by carving a new figure: the image of Rome's symbol of death—a cross! That's what he felt—death. In his despair, Joseph hammered and chipped until a man-sized cross was fully formed on the door.

At last he stood erect, his heart pounding noisily, as if to explode. His chest heaved up and down rapidly, causing him to wheeze. His robe was wet, and his dark, wavy hair stuck to his sweaty neck. He stared at his cross. He wanted to die. Death seemed sweet—his only escape from his pain. He was amazed he could hurt so badly and still be alive.

Joseph didn't realize that a death *was* taking place. It wasn't happening to his body, but rather in his soul. He had to pass through this death to self in preparation to raise the Anointed One. Joseph wasn't being analytical; he *was* dying. It was a real death.

Soon his breathing slowed and strength drained from his body. He was a man trapped in an inescapable pain, the worst kind of all: the pain of betrayal, abandonment, aloneness. He wanted to cry, but couldn't. He wanted to die, but couldn't. He was on an unreachable island as a living dead man who couldn't stop breathing.

Joseph's mallet slipped out of his hand and fell to the floor. Limply, he crawled onto the door, spread his arms and unwittingly stretched his hands to the ends of the crossbeam—like a man who had been crucified face down. Finally his anger and pride stepped aside as grief began to flow. His shoulders heaved, and he heard deep groans—sounds strange to his own ears—coming from his throat. At times he felt disconnected, as though observing the broken form of a man pleading for death. He'd rather forfeit life than face the unbearable reality of Mary's betrayal and, worse still, the wrenching choice of what to do with her.

Mary's face appeared in his mind: those large eyes pleading for trust. "Mary!" he cried out as he thought of his thunderbolt response and felt like a beast trampling upon a helpless child. Guilt tore through his soul.

But her story is too impossible! It has to be a lie! Envisioning his Mary with another man erupted fresh geysers of hate deep within him again, followed by a sense of forgiveness cascading over his heart, mellowing his spirit. It was momentarily refreshing, but was quickly dashed by the cold, unyielding reality: Mary had betrayed, then lied to him. Joseph's emotions swung back and forth across this yawning cavern of extremes. He couldn't control the billows of thought that kept tumbling through his mind. Wondering if he had gone fully mad, he fought to restore rationality: *What should I do? Call for a stoning? Disgrace her and bask in sympathy? Run away?*

Finally he fastened on an action. *I will put her away privately. Tell no one why I changed my mind about marrying her. Just go mute. She will have to bear her disgrace alone, but I will not add one drop to it. Private. . . put her away privately and keep quiet. That's what I'll do.* He was a good man, a very good man. Perhaps he would never lose the scar on his wounded soul, but he chose to wear it honorably.

Joseph lay limp, too weak to rise. Exhausted, he fell asleep.

Joseph dreamed. There was a sound like a strong wind rushing through a forest, but the sound had form. He called his thoughts to silence to see if he could hear it again. He did. He heard it clearly. It was a powerful sound. "Joseph." The sound spoke his name: "Joseph."

He shuddered from embarrassment, wondering, *Did someone enter my shop and see my crumpled form? Hear my groans?*

He lay motionless and stopped breathing to listen more intently. His dream was intense, more real than life itself. He heard the voice again. "Joseph!" The voice spoke firmly, demanding a response.

In the dream he lifted his head and responded. "Yes?"

The voice spoke in a rich, clear, commanding tone. "Joseph son of David, do not be afraid to take Mary home as your wife, because what is conceived in her is from the Holy Spirit."[5]

Joseph looked directly at the being who spoke. The image was transparent but definite, real. It had human form, but was not of this world. Its stature was royal and majestic. Joseph observed himself observing, as one does in a dream. He noticed that his emotional pain was gone.

The angel continued, "She will give birth to a son, and you are to give him the name Jesus, because he will save his people from their sins."[6]

Immediately the dream ended and the angel was gone . . .

Joseph awakened. He was not leaning on his arm as in his dream; he was still lying face down on the cross. But all was different. He knew this hadn't been a self-induced dream. It was a message from God. He *knew* it! It was solid fact to him.

Joseph pushed himself up from the door, feeling resurrection light. The death-like agony that had pressed him upon the cross had lifted. Though his robe was still wet and his hair soaked and matted, his heart was more alive than ever. He felt like he could catch a gazelle.

Standing and stretching his arms high above his head, he drew in the warm air. The sun's rays looked clean and bright slanting through the half-open door, the door where he last saw the back of Mary's white dress rippling as she ran. He mused at the small shaft of light that poured through a knothole high on the wall. Everything was beautiful.

Oh, he thought, *I must tell Mary, but how? Will she forgive the brutal wrath I spewed at her? Will she be embittered by my distrust? Is our love forever shattered?*

Joseph secured the door to his shop and went to his living quarters above to bathe.

[1]Luke 1:30-33, 35
[2]Luke 1:28
[3]Luke 1:30-33
[4]Luke 1:35
[5]Matthew 1:20
[6]Matthew 1:21

CHAPTER FOUR

Resilient Love

It was high noon on the same day. The sun paled in comparison to Joseph's freedom and joy of heart. His life had been handed back to him. Nothing seemed impossible.

Regarding the dream? He was rock sure it was a message from God, and not just a dream. He knew he had encountered an angel. Walking taller than ever, his legs felt lion strong as he bounded up the steep hill to Mary's house.

Mary's mother was at the door with her arms outstretched, but not as a warm greeting. Her body spoke of urgency. Concern furrowed her brow. Her fingers shook as she cupped Joseph's face in her hands and pled, "Joseph, can you tell me what's wrong with Mary? She was quiet at dinner last night. Went to bed very late. Ate breakfast, hardly saying a word. You know that's not like our little girl. Then, a while ago, she dashed past me covering her face with her hands and went straight to her room. She still has her face buried in her pillow, hoping I can't hear. But I can. She's weeping. Something's wrong, Joseph . . . something is very wrong."

He grasped her shoulders to give assurance. He wanted to tell her the whole story, but subdued his impetuousness. It wasn't the right time.

"I must see Mary," he said. "All will be fine if I can talk with her. But we need some time alone. Is that possible?"

Her hands slowly released Joseph's face. It was like letting go of sight and stepping into faith. Joseph was asking her to be uninvolved—to trust his judgment. She wrung her hands as she contemplated. Seconds felt like huge holes in time. She dropped her head, glancing aimlessly at Joseph's chest, and made her choice.

"I'll tell her you're here. Then I'll go to the market."

Slowly she turned and entered the house. At Mary's door, she gently announced that Joseph wanted to see her. The response sounded weak and unsure.

"Tell him I'll be there in a few moments."

"All right, Dear. I'm going to the market. Will you be okay?"

"I'll be fine, Mother. Love you . . ."

"Love you, too, Dear."

Mary's mother desired to protect and defend her daughter, but wisely gave space for Mary and Joseph to handle this problem on their own. She tried to hide her troubled heart and left.

Joseph sat in the small courtyard watching Mary's mother slowly descend the hill. He mused over what she would learn when she returned home. He thought to himself, *There goes the grandmother of the Messiah, and she doesn't even know it—yet!* Joseph gazed across the Valley of Jezreel. He visualized, as he often did, the history written in that valley: armies fighting armies, Elijah massacring Baal's prophets, Gideon defeating the Midianites.

Sensing a presence behind him, he turned and looked. Mary was leaning on the open doorpost. Her bare feet made no noise on the baked-clay floor. She still wore the white dress, although it was crumpled. Her eyes and face were puffy, and she looked drowned in weakness. She had been in the dark throes of conflict, suspended between God's extraordinary gift and Joseph's hostile rejection. One had exalted her beyond deserve and the other reduced her beyond disgrace. Her vibrant personality was showered in sadness.

"Mary!"

Joseph rose and turned toward her. She drew back slightly to let him know she didn't want to be touched. Her heart wasn't hard, just confused and full of pain.

"Mary, you must listen. Something happened."

Her eyes rose slowly toward his, although she did not look at him directly. At least she was listening. Joseph's moment had come.

"Mary, after you left my shop, I lost all self-control. I thought I would explode. I wanted to die. I felt awful shame for the way I spoke to you, but I couldn't stop the revulsion and hate that gripped me as I thought of you . . . of you, well . . . "

Mary gestured that he should not finish the sentence.

"Mary, I finally collapsed and fell into a sound sleep. . . a sleep that transported me to a world more real than this one. It didn't feel like a natural sleep. And it wasn't. It was caused by God. I'm sure of it."

He moved closer to her. She didn't draw back this time. He gestured emphatically: pressing his hands to his forehead, clapping them, waving them back and forth. Knowing he must say it right the first time, he posed like a statue for a split second in order to place his words with great accuracy.

"Mary . . . Mary, as I slept, an angel appeared to me in a dream."

Her eyes widened as her lips parted. Her entire being halted mid-breath. Hope stirred.

"You know . . . it must have been something like your experience. Only I was asleep, and you were awake."

Joseph pressed his palms against his temples, as though propping his mind with bookends. He studied her, and she studied him. He had unwittingly violated their mutual trust just hours earlier. Discrediting her as morally unfit, he had shot a cannonball of accusation directly into her heart. Now, he could afford to assume nothing. He was on trial with only one chance to prove his point. His authenticity, however, was unmistakable.

He continued: "Just like you, I can remember his very words. He said to me, 'Joseph son of David, do not be afraid to take Mary home as your wife, because what is conceived in her is from the Holy Spirit.'"[1]

"Oh . . . Joseph . . . ." Her words flowed as air brushing through a willow. Her lips barely moved.

"And, Mary, the angel went on to say, 'She will give birth to a son, and you are to give him the name Jesus, because he will save his people from their sins.'"[2]

There was a healing silence between them, like the calm after a storm. They were together again, but nothing would ever be the same. They were no longer two young people in love, asking God to bless their plans. Now, they were two young people in love, called upon to fulfill God's plan. No greater honor had come to anyone since God had handed the care of creation to Adam and Eve. Mary and Joseph were to care for the Son of God—as mother and stepfather.

The sheer magnitude of it all overwhelmed them. They couldn't speak. They stood in the hush of this holy moment, letting heaven's message filter through their souls—adrift on an eternal plan with no more to hold on to than the angelic announcements and their faith in God.

Joseph extended his hand to Mary. She laid her hand in his, and he gently drew her to his side. Once again she was his, and he was hers.

Their closeness flowed as oneness. It felt as though this supreme oneness must be flooding all of Nazareth, cascading into the Valley of Jezreel and throughout the entire world. Life felt complete. They were one with God, one with each other, one with purpose.

In the past they had often heard the words, "Hear, O Israel: The Lord our God, the Lord is one."[3] Now they were experiencing the deepest measure of God's oneness applied to them. But their oneness and silence seemed to have a music to it—a melody of peace. Peace was singing its song in their hearts, as Mary and Joseph held each other in sacred solitude.

They weren't sure how long this ethereal moment lasted. All they knew was that they wished it would never end.

Joseph broke the silence. "Yesterday we were just a young couple making plans to spend our lives together. But now God has called us to transcend romance and find the deeper meaning of love: oneness capable of bearing the weight of great responsibility."

"Nothing less will enable us to fulfill his will," Mary responded.

All too soon the sun was casting long shadows across the village of Nazareth.

[1]Matthew 1:20
[2]Matthew 1:21
[3]Deuteronomy 6:4

CHAPTER FIVE

An Unforgettable Dinner

Later that same evening Mary's mother called everyone to eat. "Mary, Joseph, your father and I are ready. Can you come now?"

The fresh smell of roast lamb stirred a hunger that had been suppressed by the past two days' events. Mary's mother tried hard not to ask any questions, although she was relieved to see such a pleasant expression on her daughter's face.

Not long into the meal, Mary announced, "Mother, Father, Joseph and I have something we must share with you."

Knowing of their integrity, the parents did not brace for bad news. But there was no way for them to prepare for what they were about to hear. Muddled voices rose and fell as neighbors walked past their home. Glowing embers in the fireplace warmly lit the room where they sat. The discussion to follow gracefully wafted on the light wind rising from the valley.

"Mother. Father." Mary looked directly at each as she spoke. "Yesterday the angel Gabriel appeared to me. He said that I am to be the mother of the Messiah!" She spoke shyly, but her confidence was convincing.

Joseph added, "I doubted Mary's words at first. Then,

today, an angel appeared to me in a dream and affirmed that this was of God."

No words ever sobered a room so suddenly. Stunned, Mary's parents exchanged wide-eyed stares, leaned forward, lowered their arms and ate no more. The four felt no fatigue, although it was day's end. Adrenaline ran high as Mary and Joseph unfolded the details of the events.

A long silence followed while Mary's parents gathered their thoughts, then her father spoke slowly, deliberately. "I believe you."

"And I as well," added her mother.

Relief flooded Mary and Joseph's hearts, and a fresh wave of conversation flowed like a babbling brook after a cloudburst. Deep into the night Mary's father asked a critical question: "When are you to conceive this child?"

Joseph replied, "I clearly remember the angel saying that it has already happened . . . perhaps yesterday when the angel appeared to Mary."

"So we need to plan for a wedding," said Mary's pragmatic mother in a matter-of-fact tone.

"Yes," Mary replied. "Yes, we do."

A concern lurked in her Abba's heart: Was Mary confused by what happened to her in light of the pagan beliefs coming from Athens about deities committing lewd acts with women? Only a daddy who held his daughter's respect could ask the next question. "Tell me, Mary, what was your experience in conceiving a child by the Holy Spirit?"

His query was pure in motive. It wasn't out of curiosity but instead concern for Mary that he asked. He wanted to prepare her for the inevitable questions people would ask in the days ahead, and he wondered if she was struggling with any unsettled issues of her own.

"I felt nothing, Abba. Nothing." Her voice was soft. She was relieved that he had asked, hoping he would shed light on this matter. She was wondering how the conception had occurred by nothing more than a pronouncement.

Her father was knowledgeable in both the Scriptures and history. He could have qualified as a rabbi. "God does everything by the power of speaking," he answered. "For instance, he spoke and creation came out of nothing. So, then, what would God need to do to send the Messiah? Speak!" He shrugged, holding his hands high and flat to emphasize how effortless such an act would be for God. His declaration hung in the air leaving no more room for question or doubt.

"Father," Mary said, "the angel said something I didn't understand."

Her father propped his elbows on the table, countenanced deep thought and listened.

"The angel said, 'The Holy Spirit will come upon you, and the power of the Most High will overshadow you.'[1] What does that mean? I experienced none of that."

"Ah, my child, that's not too hard to understand. God doesn't leave footprints where he walks.[2] Likewise, he can be closer than air and not be felt. When the Holy Spirit came upon people of old—people like Samuel and David—they never wrote of feeling the Holy Spirit, but they were certainly empowered to do mighty acts: everything from prophesying to defeating armies."

"That makes sense, Abba. I understand the part about the Holy Spirit coming upon me to speak new life into my womb, but why do you think the angel said that the power of the Most High would overshadow me?"

Mary's father leaned back in his chair—silent for the moment—rubbing his hand back and forth across his beard, as though pondering how to say something dreadful. He drew a deep, noisy breath through his nose—a cue that he was about to speak. He exhaled, then spoke in a quiet, cautionary tone.

"Mary, do you realize who this Messiah is?" The question didn't invite an answer; rather, it set the stage for the answer. "The angel told Joseph to name him Jesus because the prophets wrote that he will save his people from their sins. To do so, he must break the powers of Satan, sin and death. He must undo the damage done by Adam's sin. And that will demand a confrontation with the enemy of our souls."

"Father, what are you trying to say?"

"Mary," his voice quivered. His chest tightened as parental compassion nearly choked his words. Clearing his throat he said, "Mary, if the power of God had not overshadowed you . . ." he paused, then finished, "you would not be with us tonight. The devourer would have killed you."

"Father!" she exclaimed.

"I know, I know, my little one. The rabbis rarely speak of these things. But they know them. The Son to be born to you will have to defeat the evil one and overthrow the kings of the world. He is coming to prepare a people for his kingdom, then to set up God's kingdom on earth. You will need the shadow of divine protection throughout the rest of your life."

A huge silence followed.

"Wouldn't Satan kill all of us—just as he did Job's children—if he could?" asked Mary.

"Yes." He elaborated, "Yes, it's only by God's protection that even the Gentiles live. How much more will you need God's protection as you carry, then raise, his Son who is coming to set us free?"

Mary smiled, "So I'm safe, then?"

To give assurance to all, Mary's father said, "You are as safe as Noah and his family in the ark. There will be a terrible storm, but you will be safe."

Mary's next question took a personal turn. A hush fell over the room as she asked, "Abba, why did God choose me? I'm no different than anyone else . . ."

"Ah, my dear, the question is enormous and the answer far-reaching. But, indeed, it's important. Grace . . . grace is the only answer. No one ever deserves what God does. He acts out of grace. Your mother and I think you deserve to mother the Messiah, but it's still true that you need God's grace like everyone else. Apart from grace, there is no answer to your question."

Mary's mother spoke, "The moment we think there's something good within us that deserves God's favor, then it's no longer favor . . . it's something we deserve . . . something we earned. All we can do is rejoice in God's grace and not seek a reason, since one will never be found."

Resuming, her father extended his hand like an orator and elaborated, "Look at the acts of God's grace in history . . . how he chose things without explanation. God chose to bring the Messiah out of a lineage that included the abominable incest committed by Lot with his daughters." His voice was made richer by the grand view he had of history. Mary and Joseph stared in amazement, since this fact had eluded them.

Her father continued, "You'll remember that Lot's daughters got him drunk and lay with him in order to continue their family lineage, since there were no men available. The eldest daughter had a son whom she named Moab. He became the father of the Moabites. Generations later, Ruth, who was herself a Moabite, married Boaz. That's how she became a foremother of King David and continued the Messianic line."

Mary's mother showed great understanding when she expanded the point. "The fact that the Messiah's ancestry included incest reveals the depth of God's love and grace. God reaches to the deepest level of sin to forgive and draw people back to himself. His love cannot be affected by our sin. Despite our sin, he chose to love us, and he doesn't love us more when we're good and less when we're bad. God's love is not rooted in our conduct but, rather, in his character. God chose to extend his love to sinners at every level of failure. And there is no better evidence than his mercy upon the sin of Lot's daughters."

By now Joseph's brilliant mind was athirst. His inquisitive expression opened the way for Mary's father to expand upon the subject . . .

"Take God's grace in raising up Moses: Moses shrank from the calling, reminding God how incapable he was. But God raised him up, not to show what Moses could do for God but what God could do through Moses."

"And so it is with you, my dear," said Mary's mother, patting her daughter's arm. "God's grace is upon you. Your father and I marvel at it with you and rejoice with you."

Mary's father's voice became fuller and richer still, filling the room with theatrical presence as he boomed, "Jerusalem!" His dramatic pause caused interest to surge. How would Jerusalem fit into the history of God's grace? The question hung in the silence.

He continued, "Consider Jerusalem. It was founded by Noah's great grandson Jebus, who dragged it into the darkest dungeon of paganism. The people bowed to wooden statues and demonic gods for one thousand years until David conquered it. By grace, God chose to put his name on that city, the very city that was a haunt for demons. By grace God chose that city to be the coming world capital where the Messiah . . . the child in your womb . . . will reign!" There was a pause as everyone absorbed the impact of that truth.

"There is another reason to be added to God's grace," said her father, his voice mellowing to that of a thoughtful sage. "Sovereignty. God is sovereign. He acts alone to fulfill his purposes. God's flawless wisdom receives counsel from no one, so his reasons must be trusted and obeyed, even when not understood."

Saving his strongest point for last, with one thunderous word her father announced: "Salvation!" Again he allowed a dramatic pause to command attention.

"Mary, Joseph, the whole sacrificial system in the temple at Jerusalem makes it clear that the blood of animals cannot wash away our sins. If it could, then the priests would stop making sacrifices. The sacrifices can only teach us that God must provide the final sacrifice to take all sin away. Salvation comes as an act of God, not man."

"Yes," Mary's mother added, "just as he provided a ram for Abraham to sacrifice in place of Isaac."

"It cannot be overstated," her father continued, "that only God can provide salvation. The greatest confusion comes when people try to find something good within themselves to qualify for heaven. No, all salvation comes from God. We are still waiting on him to provide the perfect Lamb, whose sacrifice will wash away our sin."

Their discussion hadn't focused on Mary but, rather, on God. They talked about God's love, God's mercy, God's grace, God's forgiveness, God's sovereignty. It all helped Mary and Joseph adjust to the calling that was thrust upon them both within the past twenty-four hours.

The embers in the stove dimmed, and the candles flickered as they suffocated in puddles of liquid wax. Mary asked one final question. "Mother, Father, how were you able to believe me so quickly?"

Although they had not discussed it, Mary's parents smiled at each other as though of one mind. "Well," answered her father, "many Jews have had a heightened anticipation that the Messiah was soon at hand when word spread of what happened to the priest Zechariah and his wife Elizabeth six months ago."

Mary responded, "And to think, they are our relatives. Gabriel told me about this. Now I understand, Abba." It was resolved, so Mary asked no more.

At long last it was time for Joseph to leave and the family to retire. The brilliant stars almost crackled aloud as Joseph descended the hill to the room above his workshop. The air was cool and crisp, richly filling his lungs. He looked toward the sky and asked, "Why me, Lord? Why would you choose me to help raise your Son to manhood?"

The answer that flashed through his mind seemed audible. *Sovereign grace!* He could hear his father-in-law's rich baritone voice declaring, *Sovereign grace. All is by God's sovereign purpose. All is chosen by grace alone. Salvation is by God's grace alone.*

Night carried their first full day as parents of the Promised One into the annals of eternity.

[1]Luke 1:35
[2]Psalm 77:19

CHAPTER SIX

The Forerunner

Mary rose early the next morning, stepped out into the courtyard and looked across Nazareth, then beyond to the mountains across the valley. She heard the rhythmic pounding of Joseph's hammer. Routine work had to resume, despite the sacred experience they had shared the day before. The common and the sacred almost always walk side-by-side.

But this day burst upon this young woman whose life was forever changed. In one day, her simple, girlish dreams were swept away and replaced by a sovereign plan that demanded the wisdom and strength of a thousand. She would need to walk in the shadow of the Almighty all her days, as would Joseph.

Mary was preparing to discuss with Joseph her desire to visit Zechariah and Elizabeth. She had already determined to go immediately to their home.

Six months ago the story of Zechariah and Elizabeth had rocked the Judean hills. The couple enjoyed marital oneness out of mutual love and respect, but remained childless. Worse still, they were beyond their reproductive years. Historically for the Jews, childlessness was a sign of divine displeasure—a dark judgment from God—a disgrace.

Elizabeth, like Samuel's mother of old, had pled for a child, but to no avail. Her lean body and bold chin enhanced her tall, stately appearance, but childbearing vitality was gone. Zechariah had been thin and wiry from his youth, able to eat anything without gaining a pound. Over the years, he had become slightly bent in spine. He, too, had sought God to grant them a child. Now, it was too late.

The two determined not to allow their frustration to build a barrier of bitterness between them or God. Intimacy had to be on this night, since on the morrow Zechariah would begin his purification rites for serving in the temple. He was a priest and his lot had been drawn: It was his time to serve at the altar. His purification procedure reinforced that holy people are still sinners needing to be cleansed. Zechariah understood that holiness bore no merit; rather, it was his reasonable service. So his hope of redemption was in One coming who was greater than he.

After the days of purification, Zechariah rose long before dawn to begin his short journey to Jerusalem. He arrived atop the Mount of Olives as a faint glow hovered over the eastern horizon, like a mother quietly lighting a candle to awaken her children. Zechariah stood on the mount looking across the Kidron Valley and down upon the temple area. There stood the imposing structure—dark and gray and holy. The gold trim would not glitter until struck by sunlight.

He descended the mount, crossed the valley and entered through the eastern gate. Temple guards recognized him and respectfully exchanged greetings. He crossed the outer court and entered the inner court. There was a soft shuffling of feet on the cold sandstone as worshippers gathered outside the temple to pray. Zechariah felt honored to represent them before the Almighty. First, however, he had to wash and prepare sacrifices for his own sins.

His gnarled fingers trembled slightly as he lit the incense being offered to the Lord. His righteousness could not stop Adam's curse. Age had worn grooves in his skin and sapped his muscles of strength. No matter, he was resolved to serve his God to the end.

Zechariah's priesthood ancestry reached all the way back to Abijah. Now, centuries later, Zechariah was faithfully performing the same sacrifices to God. His wife understood his disciplines, since she was from the priestly ancestry of Aaron. So, for both Zechariah and Elizabeth, this was only one of many similar days of service to God. Routine, however, had not dulled their reverence. They loved God deeply and served from their hearts.

At home, Elizabeth engaged in a day that seemed like any other—nothing special. She found herself singing parts of the psalm written for the dedication of the temple:

> I will exalt you, O Lord, for you lifted me out of the depths and did not let my enemies gloat over me. O Lord my God, I called to you for help and you healed me. O Lord, you brought me up from the grave; you spared me from going down into the pit. Sing to the Lord, you saints of his; praise his holy name. For his anger lasts only a moment, but his favor lasts a lifetime; weeping may remain for a night, but rejoicing comes in the morning. You turned my wailing into dancing; you removed my sackcloth and clothed me with joy, that my heart may sing to you and not be silent.[1]

Over and over she sang the psalm. It was an awkward melody, but the author had been more concerned about the message than the meter. Elizabeth's heart was buoyant.

Back in Jerusalem, Zechariah was alone in the temple, lighting the incense. He was startled when the flame of his torch suddenly fluttered and leaned hard toward the left side of the altar, as though struck by a gust of air, but the air was still. Zechariah cocked his head to assess the strange occurrence. Stiff in spine, he turned his whole body to the right and saw a living being standing beside the altar. He dropped the torch, clutched his robe and drew back. His heart pounded, and his mouth dried completely. Fear rippled through his body like a chill. Had this been a human intruder, Zechariah would have sternly rebuked him and demanded that he exit. But this wasn't just a person; it was a presence. Zechariah wondered if he was about to die.

The angel spoke: "Do not be afraid, Zechariah; your prayer has been heard. Your wife Elizabeth will bear you a son, and you are to give him the name John."[2]

"John? . . . answered prayer? . . . It has been so long . . ." whispered Zechariah, his throat still dry and his voice quivering from shock. "John? A son named John? . . . born to Elizabeth and me?" His words were slow and measured. His eyes opened wide. He knew this just couldn't be so.

The angel continued: "He will be a joy and delight to you, and many will rejoice because of his birth, for he will be great in the sight of the Lord."[3]

Zechariah's chest heaved, both from the angel's presence and the words he spoke: a son who would be great in God's eyes. This was too much to believe.

The angel spoke further:

He is never to take wine or other fermented drink, and he will be filled with the Holy Spirit even from birth. Many of the people of Israel will he bring back to the Lord their God. And he will go on before the Lord, in the spirit and power of Elijah, to turn the hearts of the fathers to their children and the disobedient to the wisdom of the righteous—to make ready a people prepared for the Lord.[4]

Zechariah raised his hand indicating the desire to speak. Feeling unstable, he leaned on the altar. There was a long pause as he and the angel stared into each other's eyes. Zechariah had so deeply longed for a son that he refused to be vulnerable to disappointment. The angel's words were so impossible in light of reality that Zechariah dared to ask for a confirmation: "How can I be sure of this? I am an old man and my wife is well along in years."[5]

The angel straightened larger still. A dagger of insult against God was cloaked in the question. The angel's response was firm and direct: "I am Gabriel."[6]

Zechariah's breath rushed out of his body, and he could hardly inhale again. His mouth hung limply open. Standing before him was the mightiest of angels. "I am Gabriel. I stand in the presence of God, and I have been sent to speak to you and to tell you this good news."[7]

"Good news . . . Oh, yes . . . good news indeed," Zechariah repeated in a raspy whisper, not realizing he was mouthing his thoughts.

The angel kept speaking: "And now you will be silent and not able to speak until the day this happens, because you did not believe my words, which will come true at their proper time."[8]

Zechariah's face flushed with shame. He looked down at the altar, aware of his offense. It was one thing to offer incense to the unseen God, but quite another to have an angel arrive directly from God's throne, manifest and deliver a message—a message from the Almighty himself. He leaned more fully on the altar, then looked up to ask forgiveness. But the angel was gone. Wanting to regain his sense of surrounding he tried talking to himself, but only air came forth. His words were locked by an unseen hand.

About this same time in the early morn, King Herod the Great, who reigned over the Jews in Jerusalem, awakened especially agitated. He was at the palace, not a ten-minute walk from the temple.

Herod was a disgusting presence for the Jews, but he had a commanding persona and a forceful personality. He had lied, manipulated, married and murdered his way to the top. It was after the assassination of Julius Caesar that Anthony, one of Rome's Triumvirates, met with Jews at his headquarters in the Daphne Park of Antioch. Under the counsel of his advisor Hyrcanus, with one stroke of the pen, Anthony thrust Herod to the throne as king of the Jews.

Herod was grossly immoral. He had ten wives, then murdered his sons and anyone else whom he perceived as a threat to his throne. One of his wives, Miriamne, the daughter of Simon the high priest, was executed when she objected to Herod drowning her brother in the palace pool. Now, beyond madness, the king was demon possessed.

The harassing spirit that often troubled his hardened heart and tortured his deranged mind was active in Herod this morning. The power of darkness was especially disturbed this day as the angel informed Zechariah that God would bring from his loins a son who would lead many Israelites to repent and return to God. And it happened right under Herod's nose, though he knew nothing of the event. But the tormenting demon within did.

Herod muttered out loud how he had rebuilt the Jewish temple, making it grander than ever. Of course he did not share in their religion, but he wanted to weaken their resistance against him.

As Herod arose, his mood was so foul that when handed a warm drink on a silver tray, he swung violently sending the drink, the cup and the tray smashing across the sandstone floor. "Stupid, insolent, hopelessly worthless Jews!" he snarled and spit.

From the Mount of Olives, Satan sat observing Zechariah in the temple, hoping to trace and outsmart the Almighty's plan. His eyebrows furrowed as he settled his chin into his hand and tapped his temple with his forefinger. *I must kill his son,* he thought. *What can I do? Yes . . . yes, I can bring this preacher of righteousness up against those who love my ways. He'll insult them. Then he will either lose credibility, or . . . or they'll kill him. Yesss . . . that will work . . . that will work . . . yesss . . .* he hissed.

By now, Zechariah had stumbled out of the temple to face questions from those wondering why he had been delayed inside. His mouth moved, but not a whisper of sound escaped. He had to express what had happened by writing and pantomime.

"What? An angel appeared to you?" they asked. Yes, he gestured emphatically. "You're going to have a son?" they deduced from his performance. He nodded affirmatively. The temple people watched him closely in the days that followed until he finished his duties and returned to his small town in the hills not far from Jerusalem. There he lay with his wife and she conceived.

News of Zechariah's temple meeting with Gabriel, and Elizabeth's subsequent conception, traveled faster than rushing water after a torrential downpour. Everyone talked about it. And so did Zechariah and Elizabeth, though Zechariah had to write all of his thoughts. Early one evening, as the sun was setting over Jerusalem, the two stood outside of their home. Zechariah wrote, "My heart cannot find words big enough, Elizabeth, to praise God for the amazing way he answered our prayer for a child."

"Yes, my husband," said Elizabeth, "prayers we lifted years ago, then stopped, even nearly forgot. I was thinking of God's Word to Isaiah, '. . . those who hope in me will not be disappointed.'"9

Zechariah looked westward across the wilderness toward the Dead Sea, the sea that reminded him so often of their inability to have a child, and wrote: "We serve a God who blesses beyond measure. He is bringing life out of death. He is giving us more than a son to bring us joy and delight.

This son is meant to do far more than merely take away our reproach of childlessness. This child will be great in the sight of the Lord, will be filled with the Holy Spirit from birth and will turn many in Israel back to God. Elizabeth, our God is filled with abundant grace."

"Indeed he is," she replied. Elizabeth, a wise woman, added, "Often it appears as though we are missing God's perfect plan for our lives. We bore the disgrace of childlessness for all these years. Those who viewed that as a sign of wrath even doubted your right to serve as a priest. Now God has used our suffering and loss as the way to prove his power. Herein, all glory will go to him. Our God is once again showing himself faithful."

Zechariah rested his arm around Elizabeth's shoulders. They looked toward Jerusalem. The setting sun adorned the sky with shafts of rays, as though trumpeting a grand event. After a long silence between them, Zechariah wrote: "The Messiah must be coming soon, Elizabeth. He must be coming very soon . . ."

Elizabeth was six months with child when Mary conceived the Messiah, then departed Nazareth to go to the home of her relatives—the parents of John the Baptist, who would be the forerunner of the Christ.

[1]Psalm 30:1-5, 11-12
[2]Luke 1:13
[3]Luke 1:14-15a
[4]Luke 1:15b-17
[5]Luke 1:18
[6]Luke 1:19a
[7]Luke 1:19
[8]Luke 1:20
[9]Isaiah 49:23

CHAPTER SEVEN

The Magnificat

First Mary traveled southward through the Jordan Valley to Jericho, then turned west on the old Jericho road leading up to the city of David. From Jericho it was a fourteen-mile trek through the mountainous wilderness that rose about thirty-four hundred feet above that city. Finally she crested the Mount of Olives. There her eyes beheld Jerusalem—the city of God—resting like a crown on top of Mount Moriah. She wanted to refresh her body and soul before her visit with her relatives. More so, she wanted to absorb the rich, historical scene spreading before her eyes.

Strong in body and spirit, she took a long drink of cold water from a well and sat down on the ground facing westward. Unafraid, she wanted to be alone—just she and God. She looked down upon Mount Moriah, where sat the temple: austere, quiet, commanding. It drew a special reverence from her heart, a worship that was different from what nature inspired. This was where Jews acknowledged their need of a Savior by offering sacrifices for their sins. This was where the heavenly Father of her child chose to meet with his people—Israel, especially when they sought him with all their hearts.

The historical events that occurred on this mount animated in her mind as she recalled her parents' scriptural teaching. These events were important to her, since they foreshadowed the One whom she bore in her womb. She visualized Abraham on this very mountain laying his son upon a makeshift altar of wood, obediently raising a knife high above his head to plunge it into Isaac's heart, only to have God stay his hand and provide a ram for sacrifice instead.

She drew her knees up to her chin and wrapped her arms around them. The story's meaning came alive. Her thoughts were vivid: *God wanted Abraham to sacrifice his heart, not his son, and Abraham proved his wholehearted love for God by his willingness to obey. He also proved his faith in God to raise his son up to life again.* She felt as though she could hear God's voice in the wind telling Abraham that his faith and love had been tested and proven true.

She shifted her chin more comfortably on her knees to contemplate more deeply: *It was God who provided the sacrifice . . . God! All salvation comes from God alone, just like Abba said. We can do no more than love, worship, believe and obey him with all our hearts. He provides the sacrificial death for our sins. He alone cleanses from sin and gives new life.*

Her eyes focused on the temple. She thought of the millions of animals that had been offered to God through the centuries and of the blood that flowed from the temple into the Kidron Valley. Her refined nature never liked the thought of animals dying in such a manner, but she realized the importance of the lessons taught by the sacrifices. She knew that of all the animals slain, not one could take away sin. Their deaths served only to repeatedly teach the lesson that while sin brings death God brings redemption. Mary's mind wandered back across the pages of her training, seeking to more fully understand why animals were sacrificed.

She remembered God's words to Adam warning that death would result should he eat of the forbidden fruit from the tree of the knowledge of good and evil. "Yes," she whispered softly, "and each animal that has died has reinforced that truth. But God does not want his people to perish, so he demonstrated through the sacrifices that he would accept a substitute to die for us all. Yet the prophets said the blood of bulls and goats is not a sufficient sacrifice, so God must provide his own—one sufficient to take away Israel's sins."

At that realization, she leaned back, straightened her legs, placed one hand on her womb and said aloud, "Oh, God . . . Oh, God. It's my son. Oh my Holy Father . . . it's your Son. He is the sacrifice. As the angel said to Joseph, we are to call him Jesus, for he will save us from our sins."

Mary was sitting near a gnarled olive tree that had two limbs protruding from opposite sides of the trunk, casting a shadow shaped like a cross. It reminded her of the cross Joseph had shaped on their door in his hour of despair. Understanding that the price of sin is death, she wondered what that would mean for her son. *In what way will he make the final sacrifice for sin?*

As she meditated on this, an unexpected wave of sadness washed over her, and she swallowed hard, fighting back the tears. The true significance of the angel's announcement was finally clear to her. Though she had been chosen to be the mother of the Messiah, the child she bore would not be hers to keep. She would have to be willing to give him up, perhaps even unto death. It was a bittersweet moment as she relinquished her own ideals—of life, motherhood, the future—for the sake of God's sovereign plan.

Mary the youth was transformed into Mary the woman— compressing years of maturity into moments.

She scanned the panoramic view of Jerusalem from north to south. Herod's palace and the Jewish temple were superimposed upon the grid of buildings: tall, short, narrow, wide—most, joined together. Narrow stone streets pulsed as people coursed through them like the life-giving blood of the city. The stones glistened, having been shined from the endless flow of shuffling feet. The sun was now high and shadows were short, and the sandstone city was baked in gold. She spoke out loud: "You, my

Son, will some day reign in glory over the whole world from this, your capital."

She sat for hours thinking, praying, absorbing. At long last, her poetic mind was ready to capture the impressions of her heart in prose. The words flowed with grand eloquence as she prayed them out loud:

> My soul glorifies the Lord and my spirit rejoices in God my Savior, for he has been mindful of the humble state of his servant. From now on all generations will call me blessed, for the Mighty One has done great things for me—holy is his name. His mercy extends to those who fear him, from generation to generation. He has performed mighty deeds with his arm; he has scattered those who are proud in their inmost thoughts. He has brought down rulers from their thrones but has lifted up the humble. He has filled the hungry with good things but has sent the rich away empty. He has helped his servant Israel, remembering to be merciful to Abraham and his descendants forever, even as he said to our fathers.[1]

"My Savior," she softly said over and over. "I am the human mother, but he is the divine Savior. *My* Savior . . . not just the world's."

Her Abba's rich voice echoed in her mind saying, *It is all by grace that you are chosen, my dear. All by grace.* She recalled King David, who wrote of God stooping down to make him great.[2] She realized anew that God calls the humble in heart to be the instruments of his great acts, since he can share his glory with none. She looked toward the bright blue sky and whispered, "O, Jehovah, God, thank you. I praise and honor you, O my God."

Mary found herself humming the psalm used in the dedication of the temple as she pondered the deep truths commanding her mind . . .

In his little carpentry shop in Nazareth, Joseph was putting the final touches on his latest piece of workmanship. He stepped back from the table to admire a new door, ornamented with carvings of sheep, birds and vines with clusters of grapes. He felt a tinge of pride as he said to himself, *It's more beautiful than the original design I crafted.*

But Joseph's humility quickly returned when he gazed upon the scrapheap in the corner of the room. There, leaning against the wall, was the door he had first made, then destroyed, in his bitter despair. He looked at the ugly gouges that formed the cross—a grim reminder of his yearning to die just a few short days ago. In stark contrast, the new door resting on the worktable was testament to Joseph's renewed spirit. Those longings for death seemed foreign to him now, as he anticipated his life with Mary and the role he would play as the earthly father of the coming Messiah.

He longed for Mary's return home, so that he could finally present the door to her as a wedding gift.

It was late afternoon when Mary prepared to continue her journey. A shepherd walked past, herding sheep toward Bethlehem. The flock formed a long, fluffy gray line of living wool, slowly meandering along the path toward a safe place to rest for the night.

The shepherd had one sheep draped over his shoulders— one that was aggressive, a natural-born leader. He had intentionally broken its leg and was carrying it on his shoulders until it healed. Though this was a harsh practice, shepherds learned that by caring for the sheep as it healed, it would bond and stay near him for the rest of its days. Then the shepherd could use this sheep to lead the flock, knowing it would direct all others to follow the shepherd.

Mary couldn't help but think of the great men and women of God throughout history—all broken by God, bound to God, then used by God.

As Mary watched the flock trail over the horizon, she quoted out loud:

> The Lord is my shepherd, I shall not be in want. He makes me lie down in green pastures, he leads me beside quiet waters, he restores my soul. He guides me in paths of righteousness for his name's sake. Even though I walk through the valley of the shadow of death, I will fear no evil, for you are with me; your rod and your staff, they comfort me. You prepare a table before me in the presence of my enemies. You anoint my head with oil; my cup overflows. Surely goodness and love will follow me all the days of my life, and I will dwell in the house of the Lord forever.[3]

No sooner had the sheep passed when she heard hooves thundering, whips cracking and men shouting. The ground trembled beneath her feet. She spun around to see a thick cloud of dust approaching. Out of the billowing wall of gray cloud flashed the bright metallic edges of spears mounted in the front of chariots. The line of warriors was long, obviously escorting someone important.

Mary barely had time to think when the pounding procession halted before her. The dust continued forward, then dissipated. She saw dozens of horses tossing their heads, snorting and pawing the ground. The chariots rocked as horses stomped and pranced, their reins held fast by soldiers wearing leather helmets and chest pads. All eyes fastened upon her. Perplexed, the soldiers waited to see why they were stopped to look at a simply clad girl—just a girl, nothing more.

The chariot in the middle of the line was more ornate and larger than the rest, with a gold insignia of Rome on each side. A handsomely aged, massive man with a full beard stood in the chariot glaring at Mary. He studied her as though eyeing an enemy.

This man was King Herod the Great! . . . broad shouldered, thick in chest and intimidating.

He was being troubled by the resident demon who hated this girl. Thinking the inner turmoil was no more than his own instincts, Herod couldn't understand why this girl bothered him. The moment his eyes lighted upon her he felt disdain. He turned to bark an order for a soldier to kill her, but then suddenly stopped. Instead, he got off the chariot and stepped toward Mary. He stood before her, his right hand tightly gripping his sword. *Kill her yourself!* taunted the demon. *Kill her!* Mary's heart raced as the eternal moment stretched on. Finally Herod turned and climbed back into the chariot, scowling, still fighting the phantom within. It was absolutely ridiculous, even to him, to despise this unsophisticated young girl.

The absurdity of the struggle awakened a rare stroke of wisdom in Herod, and, cracking his whip over the horses, he yelled fiercely to move on. The long line of soldiers followed suit, cracking their whips. Fear drove the horses to dig their hooves into the ground and lunge forward, scattering large clods of turf.

Mary watched as the cyclone of rumbling wheels and swirling dust moved through the Kidron Valley and into the city of Jerusalem. Gradually, the ground stopped trembling.

The mighty angel of God who had been standing behind King Herod sheathed his sword of war, which had been drawn and raised high. This young girl before him—the mother of the Messiah—was his charge. The angel followed ever close as Mary turned and started toward the home of Elizabeth and Zechariah.

Late that evening Mary reached her cousin's home. Excitement erupted upon her arrival. Only Mary could greet people as though dark nights didn't exist. More than that, however, was the sacredness the family attached to her visit. And so it was when she greeted Elizabeth.

Elizabeth heard Mary's voice and instantly felt her womb bulge and recede as the child she carried leaped for joy. She responded to Mary's greeting in a loud voice: "Blessed are you among women, and blessed is the child you will bear! But why am I so favored, that the mother of my Lord should come to me? As soon as the sound of your greeting reached my ears, the baby in my womb leaped for joy. Blessed is she who has believed that what the Lord has said to her will be accomplished!"[4]

Mary responded by reciting the song that poured from her heart on the Mount of Olives. The two women felt profoundly unworthy to be bearing the two men who would bring salvation to the world: John, the forerunner announcing the final sacrificial Lamb, and Jesus, the Lamb of God himself.

After staying with Elizabeth and Zechariah about three months, Mary returned home. She found herself singing a song that was born in her heart:

"The thought that you would call a girl, a sinner such as I,
To birth your Son, your only Son, compels my heart to cry."

The trek back to Nazareth was typically hot and dusty. Mary found herself fatiguing more easily on her return journey. She frequently stopped to rest under the shade of a tree or get a cool drink from the Jordan River. Finally, she passed through the eastern crevice in the mountains surrounding her hometown. She was anxious to visit Joseph at his shop before ascending the western hill to her home. Within days, they would be married.

"Mary," he said with delight, when he saw her standing in the doorway. They embraced.

Mary excitedly relayed to Joseph the details of her time with Elizabeth and Zechariah. Though Joseph shared her enthusiasm, it was clear that he was troubled. Concerned she asked, "What's wrong?"

"I'm almost sorry that you have returned to hear the awful things some are saying about our child. Some say you went away to hide your shame. Others look pitifully at me as though

I was betrayed and am too stupid to admit it. Some people even try to guess who the real father is. It's been a nightmare."

"I can imagine, Joseph. I'm sorry that this has been such a difficult time for you."

"I'm fine, Mary, I know the truth. I love you, and I'm committed."

During the following months, as the child grew in Mary's womb, she and Joseph spent many evenings with her parents, discussing the Scriptures. They had the dual responsibility of serving the will of God to raise the Messiah, while also building their own lives together. Mary's parents served as a stabilizing force, often sharing in long discussions, encouraging them with biblical examples of how God's people throughout history handled unique calls to divine duty.

It was nine months after Gabriel's visit that Mary—now great with child—and Joseph departed Nazareth for Bethlehem. Nazareth disgorged itself as virtually the entire populace also made the journey to satisfy the demand for a census made by Caesar Augustus. This was the first census taken while Quirinius was governor of Syria. Joseph had to sign the census because he belonged to the line of David.[5]

[1]Luke 1:46-55
[2]Psalm 18:35
[3]Psalm 23
[4]Luke1:42-45
[5]Luke 2:1-5

CHAPTER EIGHT

The Late Arrival

Except for an unexplainable restlessness among the sheep, the approaching night was quiet and calm. The sun was sinking beneath the western horizon, drawing the brightness out of the sky and leaving a canopy of indigo blue soon to turn inky black. The air was clear, swept clean of summer haze. The rising moon was sharp and crisp, and the spray of emerging stars touched the chord of awe deep within the soul.

Reposing on a steep slope across a ravine from Bethlehem, the herders watched the flaming lights of the distant town flicker sleepily. The clear night permitted them to stay in the fields and not return the sheep to the caves near Bethlehem for safety. Having built a fire, they unfurled blankets, drew their robes more tightly around them and sat talking in low tones. Sometimes they were amazingly philosophical, but generally they placated their boredom with small talk.

On this night, some of the shepherds began to reminisce about the days when King David shepherded on these same hills, almost one thousand years earlier. They discussed how he separated himself from the other shepherds to write poetry and sing to God. A couple of shepherds leaned into the wind as though hoping to hear him strum the lute and sing his psalms across the ages. Many of the men mocked the refinement of this discussion. It agitated them.

After a long pause, one shepherd said, "This is the very place where God found David and took him from herding sheep to commanding armies, then on to leading the nation."

Some of the shepherds lay on their backs, locking their fingers behind their heads. They felt fortunate to be out on these mountains. God was extravagant when creating this place: rugged hills bulging skyward, weather that wildly changed from tranquility to terror, brooks that hurriedly cascaded to satisfy thirst on the plains below, lions with kingly ferocity, stars sparkling against black infinity.

Some shepherds responded to it mindlessly; others, like David of old, were transformed by it. A young, spiritually sensitive shepherd broke the silence. "Just think," he said, "this is where David heard messages in his soul and came to know the Creator of it all. This place enlarged David's understanding of God, and David's God enlarged him. And this is our God too."

"That's wonderful, lad," said a shepherd in a paternal tone.

Another one laughed crudely, but only loud enough to be heard by his friends who despised such talk.

Suddenly every shepherd sat straight up as if on cue. Something unseen shattered the calm. One flock of sheep darted, then stopped as though spooked by a presence. Ears perked. Eyes widened. Nostrils flared. Every sense searched for the danger. That flock's shepherd rushed to them, eyes scanning in all directions, trying to penetrate the encroaching night. There was no visible danger. Then another flock bolted in like fashion and abruptly froze. The shepherds ran to various posts around the sheep and called to each other from different directions.

"See anything?"

"What's disturbing them?"

"Nothing. There's nothing."

"Nothing over here either."

A third flock spooked; bleating and snorting flooded the air. Their only defense was to bawl, but that increased their vulnerability. There had to be an unseen predator crouching, crawling, craving. The shepherds herded the sheep closer together.

They returned to sit cross-legged near the fire, continuing their vigilant watch. They held clubs, mustering their courage to fight should a ferocious wolf attack from the bush or, worse still, a lion. They hoped to bluff the creature before it dragged a squalling victim into the night.

One shepherd caught sight of a slow, dark object moving on the distant ridge, over on the road that snaked seven miles from Jerusalem to Bethlehem. The fading light on the horizon silhouetted a lonesome form trudging toward town.

Certainly this wasn't the threat; it was too far away, too small, too quiet. The shepherds squinted to assess that the object had legs. It was a person walking in front of a donkey, and either a large bundle or a person was on the donkey's back. Loose clothing flapped lifelessly. The haggardly pair moved with a tired, pathetic gait.

"Wonder who that is?" posed one of the shepherds.

"Probably a latecomer for the census," said another.

Thinking of the distance a third one said, "A Galilean is my guess."

The sheep continued bawling and pacing in frenzied circles. The night was strangely charged, as though unseen forces had amassed bringing their own agitation.

Seven miles away, in the city of Jerusalem, a disturbance of another sort took place.

"Summon the singer with the lute," commanded a palace guard. "The king is troubled again."

King Herod the Great was often given to fitful nights, ever since executing his wife. All were mystified at his ability to build grand edifices and rule over the Jews despite his madness.

Fevered, King Herod paced the palace wall in Jerusalem. He glowered toward Bethlehem—eyes not focused—intensely staring. His forehead beaded with sweat, and his chest heaved and caved rapidly. He loosened his robe to cool the fire within. It was the messenger again, that terrible unseen messenger who came from an unknown world, speaking horrors to his mind. This night was the worst ever. The message wasn't clear, just a dreadful sense of threat . . . he knew it meant something, but nothing was clear.

His response was predictable. Falling back upon his manipulative, murderous ways, he brooded over whom he should kill to satisfy the enflamed presence within. Preserving his power was all that mattered. People were dispensable—mere steppingstones to achieve his desires.

Bethlehem—he couldn't stop staring toward Bethlehem. What could that place matter? It was just a tiny town. His gaze had never fallen there before. Unexplainably, the threat in his soul came from the direction of Bethlehem.

A musician began to strum his lute, but there was no relief.

Herod the Great tore his robe open to the waist, shouting, "Go away!" The lutenist fled, leaving Herod alone to fight the alien he allowed to rule his heart.

Exhausted, Mary and Joseph finally ended their arduous journey to Bethlehem, having crossed the same eighty miles Mary traversed on her visit to Elizabeth and Zechariah. Joseph, meager in earthly wealth, had walked while Mary had ridden a common donkey. Memories lay within them like treasures of the deep: the hopeful words of angels, the prophetic words of Elizabeth, the cruel words of villagers.

Torches dimly lit the streets, their small flames dancing in the breeze, sending shadows pirouetting on the buildings. Dogs growled and barked at the night. A few straggling merchants walked quickly to their homes, mumbling in low tones. Thousands had come to Bethlehem to sign the census commanded by Caesar Augustus, and the inns bulged with humanity. A deep sleep was settling across the town. Most of the visitors wanted to rise early, finish their business and start for home. There were no late-night attractions in the little town.

Joseph grasped a small mallet hanging by the door of an inn and softly knocked.

"Joseph," said Mary, "I think my time is soon. I'm tired. Please hurry."

He pounded harder. A muffled voice sputtered on the other side of the door. Joseph heard the dull sound of wood sliding on wood as the safety bar was pulled back. Hinges creaked as the innkeeper—a short, round man—opened the door, rubbing his face. His mouth was buried beneath a thick, drooping mustache, and his eyes were hidden under massive, straggly brows. Giving Joseph no chance to speak, the man gruffly expressed his irritation: "There's no room here. Every room's full. No room anywhere. Don't know what to tell you."

He tucked his chin, exhaled to end the conversation, and started to close the door.

"Joseph!" Mary blurted out, the urgency edging her voice.

Joseph gently touched the door, not wanting to further agitate the man. "Sir, please listen. We have come from Nazareth, and my wife is heavy with child. Is there anything you can do for us? We're simple people. We don't need much. Is there anything . . . anything you can do?"

The innkeeper stared at Joseph in disbelief. Beneath his indifferent exterior was a man in whom compassion felt at home. He slowly rubbed his hand across his mustache, sighed deeply and clucked his tongue as he considered Joseph's request. His grand display of profound deliberation offered better promise than the sound of a door slamming shut, so Joseph waited patiently.

"All right," he finally said, "there's only one thing I can do. In the back," he pointed over his shoulder, "are the shepherds' caves. There's no bed there. It's rough, and it might not smell too good." The man lowered one eyebrow, wrinkled his nose and grinned. Joseph was encouraged by the mild attempt at humor. "It may not be too clean either . . . you know, the shepherds take their flocks there in bad weather. But this is a beautiful night," he continued as his round eyes scanned the heavens. "I'm sure they won't be back tonight. It's not a palace, but it's shelter. Want it?"

"Yes, sir, we do."

"Well, then, I'll get you some blankets. There's plenty of straw to use for a bed—lots of wood for a fire too. You can take care of that, can't you?"

"Yes, sir. And thank you, sir, very much."

The innkeeper glanced at Mary. She looked tired and worn. Her body was draped in loose garments, and only her face showed. It was swollen, as was her whole body, providing life for two. Her lips gently formed the words, *Thank you.* Gladness touched the man's heart.

CHAPTER NINE

Night of Holy War

By now, the evening's glow was snuffed out by night. Stars were brightly strewn across the velvety sky.

As Mary and Joseph settled into the cave, they heard the distant bleating of sheep and the vague sounds of shepherds' voices from the hill across the way.

"What's with these sheep?" griped one shepherd. "Why do they keep bawling?"

"This makes me nervous," said another staring intently at the black hills. "There's no sign of a killer on the prowl, but animals sense things that humans can't. Makes me real nervous."

In Jerusalem Herod paced like a caged lion from one end of the palace wall to the other. He never took his eyes off the dull glow from Bethlehem's light reflecting against the sky. When walking away from it, he watched over his shoulder. When walking toward it, he glared as though set to attack it. He was consumed with a sense of threat—dreadful, nauseating threat.

The messenger in his soul was unbearably restless, warning him that he might be overthrown—perhaps, *tonight!*

There was another disturbance in Jerusalem—a holy one. Simeon couldn't sleep. He thrashed about in bed, goaded by a deep disturbance urging him to pray. For years, hope drove him to watchfully pray for the Messiah to come. He had even received a special revelation from the Holy Spirit that he would not die before seeing the Lord's Christ.[1]

On many nights, Simeon had been awakened by a call to prayer stirring within him, but tonight it was different— much stronger than before. Troubled, he rose from his bed, robed, strapped on his sandals and left for the temple. His steps hastened as his cane tapped against the grooved sandstone streets of Jerusalem. Reaching the outer court, he saw Anna, who was herself crossing the courtyard to enter her place of prayer.

Anna the prophetess was the daughter of Phanuel of the tribe of Asher.[2] She was a small, lean woman, bent over with age. Many years earlier her husband had died after only seven years of marriage. She then devoted the rest of her life to live in the temple in order to fast and pray for the coming of the Messiah.

"Anna," Simeon called out, "what do you suppose is happening? I was awakened with the deepest urgency warning me to pray."

"Yes, yes, Simeon, I feel the same urgency. Surely, something very important is happening. I don't know if it is something good or evil, but my heart is distressed beyond measure."

Simeon and Anna parted to two different places in the temple to lift to God the thunderous disturbance in their spirits. They didn't need to know what to pray for, just that they were to be faithful in prayer—*now!*

Simeon wanted no comfort to ease the agony in his soul. He threw his body upon a stone bench along the temple wall. His skin felt clammy, and his stomach trembled as if sick, though he was not ill. He labored to breathe as his heart pounded to counter the pressure coming from the unseen world. "O God, O God!" he cried. Heaving words from deep within, he continued, "O God, what is it? Can my body survive? What's happening? I do not understand, but I pray for your will to be established on earth."

Soon groans replaced his words, which were too limiting for such intercession. He was drawn into heaven's travail, battling heart-to-heart with God against the forces of hell itself.

In her secluded corner of the temple, Anna lifted her hollowed face heavenward knowing that the crushing weight upon her was more than her aged body could bear. Years of fasting and prayer, however, emboldened her with confidence in God's strength, and her faith swelled mightier than the strength of the enemy. She knew a war had erupted in the heavenly realms that demanded her entire being to be part of the battlefield—intercession in its deepest form. "My precious and faithful Jehovah, God. I give you my life for the battle of this night. I know I shall survive by your power. Rise up and by your might establish the victory that lies within your heart. Above all, I cry out to you for the safe coming of the Anointed One."

"Awake! Awake! Come see!" Far to the east two Magi ran to the home of their friend, their voices frenzied with excitement as they reported the discovery. The group quickly gathered at their observation post. There it hung, bright and beautiful—a star never before seen, hovering in the eastern sky toward Jerusalem. Unique to the constellations, the star appeared to have been guided there by a sovereign hand as a message from heaven itself. Having studied the Jewish prophets, the Magi were convinced that a Jewish king would emerge to rule the world. To them, this star marked his birth. They decided to visit Jerusalem in search of the king . . . but not yet. That would take careful planning and preparation

In the cave, Joseph arranged a huge pile of straw, then unfurled two rough blankets over the stack. He built a small fire that snapped and crackled with newness. Mary sat quietly, not feeling well. She knew the child could come this night. Joseph helped her lie upon the makeshift bed, bunching the straw to elevate her head and knees. Then for a short while, the two reminisced over the fast-paced events of the previous nine months.

It wasn't long before she felt her first contraction. Her time was near.

Outside of the cave, in the spirit realm, a far different scene was unfolding. Powers of darkness and powers of light were amassing: angels of darkness on the hills just across the way and angels of light before the mouth of the cave. A cosmic war was about to erupt over the child who was soon to be born.

The conflict actually started in eternity past when Lucifer (whose biblical name was Day Star), the most beautiful of all the angels, led a rebellion against God. One third of the angels followed his mutiny and were thrown out of heaven. Lucifer eventually donned titles such as "Satan" and "devil" as he headed his fallen kingdom.

For reasons known only to God, the war of eternity past was allowed to penetrate time and spill onto planet Earth. Satan, furious to think God would create a race superior to himself, was bent upon an overthrow. Unable to dethrone God, Satan then focused his efforts on destroying God's prized creation—mankind.

The assault that first broke out in the Garden of Eden was escalating to epic proportions on this night. Satan understood that the coming baby was Jesus, whose name means "he will save his people from their sins." Satan was resolved to stop this birth.

It was at this moment that an image appeared on high, beyond earth's heavens, visible to the spirit world alone. "A great and wondrous sign appeared in heaven: a woman clothed with the sun, with the moon under her feet and a crown of twelve stars on her head."[3]

The imposing sight intimidated the powers of darkness. Satan had commanded them all to gather on the hills near Bethlehem. Awaiting the arrival of the Prince of Darkness, they swarmed in wild confusion—deeply agitated by the vision of the woman looming above their heads. The spirits were frantic, having never been summoned en masse before, nor having ever seen such a sign in the sky.

If the woman in the sky seemed dramatic, so would Satan's appearance be upon his arrival. There was no way for them to prepare for the sight they were about to see. He was rushing to Bethlehem shaped in a gruesome form that would reveal the depth of his hopeless depravity.

Out on the fields the shepherds ran frantically in various directions trying to control their flocks. Never had the sheep been in such utter panic. Still, there was no visible cause. They had no perception of the menacing gathering that was unnerving the sheep.

Finally Satan appeared, and the demonic delirium settled. All stared intently at him, seeking to interpret his form. There stood the master deceiver appearing as a red dragon with seven heads—a beast symbolic of his character and conduct. The reddish hue of his skin, which was crusty with scales, spoke of his murderous heart. Seven heads bulged from seven elongated necks, each representing one of his seven major wars against the Almighty[4]—this night being one of them. His fierce image was reflected in the heavenly realms, hovering before the woman.

Every principality, power, demon and wicked spirit fell before him as though worshipping, but they were actually groveling in fear of his presence. None spoke. Most of these dark angels rarely saw Satan, since only the principalities reported directly to him. The halls of hell echoed with emptiness, and the rest of the earth experienced relief while the agents of undiluted evil were gathered at Bethlehem—their vile leader in full strut.

Satan's highly structured kingdom of darkness arranged itself in descending order of rank and authority. Near him were the principalities and powers, known as rulers. Next came the powers and authorities, followed by lower powers and authorities of this world and finally spiritual forces of this dark world.[5] All were cowering in terror.

Satan realized that he had to brace his forces. "Look . . . Look!" he roared, pointing to the woman in the heavenly realms. "Do you know what she represents?" he barked, as though they were responsible. "That woman represents all the people God wants to rob from us. Do not fear her! Soon you will see me towering before her," he declared so as to assure victory over her.

Fury fed fury. Satan's hate flowed like liquid fire. Not one demon budged. Not even the principalities dared to respond, fearful of both the unsettling view in the heavenly realms and their commander's wrath. Determined to show them the urgency of this night, Satan continued: "Do you see the twelve stars on her crown? That represents the tribes of Israel. God is sending through Israel the One who desires to undo us. That's why God is coming tonight . . . to destroy all we have worked so hard to build."

Satan turned in circles, slashing the air with his finger, attempting to shred God's intention. His fevered pitch indicated the seriousness of the coming battle. "That woman down there in the cave . . . do you know who she is? Do you know why she is here?" His questions were weighted with condemnation, as though the demons should have done something to stop her. "God plans to step on this earth in human form. We all heard him say it through the prophets." By this point Lucifer was screaming. "And this . . . this is the woman through whom he plans to be born in order to take people from our control—to save them from us! . . . And, he's coming tonight! Tonight!"

Leaving nothing to chance, he raised a clawed fist and shouted, "We must stop it! We will kill the infant tonight! We will! We must! Tonight . . . tonight!"

Renewed in their courage, the warriors of darkness lifted a bone-chilling wave of chants, "Tonight, we kill the child . . . tonight, we kill the child . . . tonight we kill the child." The chanting rose like a tidal wave, though the angels of light gathered at the cave were not intimidated by it.

Satan mused: "It will be easy to kill God while reduced to infancy. Easy! Do you hear me? Eeeasy! There is no way for him to overpower us now. God had the power to defeat us in the past, but this is our night of victory! He threw us out of heaven, but tonight we will throw him off this planet. This is our realm! I am the prince and the power of the air. Here I reign. Here God dies!"

To think of an infant up against this evil throng made them laugh. They laughed . . . harder and harder, louder and louder, and shook their fists toward heaven in mockery. Soon a roar of mockery swelled and was heard throughout the universe. They hadn't laughed this deeply since Lucifer, wearing serpentine attire, enticed the first parents, Adam and Eve, to eat the forbidden fruit.

Despite their sinister mirth, however, the image of the woman in the heavenly realms remained steadfast. Their laughter slowly died, though Satan held a long, smug grin, convinced that his hordes would win. A victory on this night would end mankind's chance of escaping his grasp. All mankind would be eternally doomed, forever abandoned to live under the authority of his depraved dictatorship.

One of the principalities mustered the courage to address their leader. "Great are you, O Satan. We remember well your past splendor, but revere you as greater than ever. We understand what the woman and the twelve stars represent, but why is the woman clothed in the sun? What does that mean?"

Bitter cursing interspersed Satan's explanation about the sun. Fear that an explanation might in some way show weakness, or endorsement of God's plan, gave him grave concern. "You know that I offered to Adam and Eve the very same freedom we fought to gain—the freedom of self-rule. I told them that they could be as God, and that there would be no consequence of death." He formed his words as though chewing on his cleverness when he added, "They listened. The fools listened indeed."

Dull laughter rippled through their ranks, and they repeated the words, "They listened, they listened."

Satan resumed his speech: "They were shocked when God threw them out of the garden and into the world of our control. The putrid couple was bewildered by the unfamiliar feelings of jealousy, pride and hate that stripped them of the sickening innocence they had known." Satan rolled his next words like juicy morsels as he spoke them, "They didn't know until it was too late that these are the building blocks of independence! Independence from the Creator!"

"Yes! Yes!" cheered the demons as they broke into applause.

Satan paused dramatically, then went on: "But some were too weak to pay the price of our freedom. They cried out to God for forgiveness . . . sniveling wretches. As you all know, God demands that his subordinates wear robes of righteousness. Those are the robes we threw off when we draped ourselves in robes of our own design. We set our own standards—which are *no* standards! Freedom . . . that's freedom!"

Approving cheers reverberated among the hills. The stench of Satan's deception smelled sweet, at least momentarily. Darkness almost seemed to glow. When the cheering died, a large principality asked, "Since the humans wear our garments of self-rule, how can God take them back?"

Satan blew a loud snort of disgust and answered, "It repulses me, but God plans to save them. But first, he had to show them their inability to escape us on their own. They lacked the strength. They failed the Ten Commandments. Ha! We had a hand in that."

Lucifer's bloodthirsty eyes bulged as he continued: "Ten Commandments! How dare God give us minds and wills only to chain us to rules of his own making. It's said that his laws reflect his heart. So what? I want my own rules to reflect me. ME! I say that no rule is the best kind of rule. Only then can one be free for self-expression. When I establish my own rule, which is no rule at all, then I set myself up as my own god. And the same goes for you. You become your own god!"

Pride puffed every breast, making the gathering look enlarged.

Satan then turned away from the crowd, pointed back into history and said, "Now do you understand why the prophets talked about a new covenant? Having proven that mankind could not gain its own salvation, God is about to offer it free— a free gift of righteousness. God plans to clothe them in his Son's righteousness. That's what the sun symbolizes—redeemed people clothed in the gift of his Son's righteousness."

A wave of understanding flowed across the satanic ranks. They admired their leader's mastery of theology, although they despised what it meant. Satan, Lord of the Flies, watched his garbage dwellers agonizingly gnash their teeth and wring their hands.

After a pause, another principality asked why the woman was standing on the moon. Satan's face twisted into a scowl. His voice became terse, revealing the insult found in the answer. "The moon, you ask? Why is she standing on the moon? That's supposed to be the things we teach people. God insists that we are deceivers and that only he is truth. Just as the moon is an ever-shifting reflection of the sun and has no power to give light of its own, we are being mocked as though shifty and unable to give light. That's not true! We give the light of self-rule. Was I not the angel of light?"

The entire gathering responded with the crashing sound of violent waves, "You, O Satan, are the angel of light."

Then a deep silence fell as Satan slowly lifted his eyes toward the image that stood higher than the sky. A straight, black line crossed his brow as he glared at it. Suddenly the grand gathering of evil felt insecure. Their doomed commander spoke, "The battle will be soon. Get ready now!"

The woman in the sky made a shrill cry that penetrated the universe and quieted the demonic reveling. Satan heard it and snarled with special hatred. The cry signaled the start of the war that was boiling to erupt between the forces in the heavenly realms. The woman was pregnant and cried out in pain as she was about to give birth.[6]

At the same instant, young Mary shifted her position on the straw bed and cried out as her contractions became severe. The evil one's eyes widened like a wolf spotting the birth of a lamb. Cruelty dripped from his lips as he craved to pounce. But the moment Mary cried, the sound of a mighty wind was heard—a sound greater than that of a thousand tornadoes in one. It was heaven's army finalizing its stance over the cave, planted firmly between the young couple and the hordes of hell. Satan became livid. His legions drew back.

Mary cried again, and at once both heaven and hell unsheathed their swords.

The greatest war since Satan's expulsion from heaven exploded as his forces fought desperately against the coming of God on this night. Earthly eyes could not see the war. It was taking place in the spirit realm, invisible and inaudible to the natural realm. But, true to spiritual conflict, Mary and Joseph felt the war as they experienced unbearable pressures against their bodies and minds. With the rejection at the inn, God had wisely orchestrated this epic event to occur within a cave, where thick stone walls would protect the couple's dignity.

Inside the cave—the solitary epicenter for this cosmic conflict—Mary's cries intensified as the baby in her womb became hell's target.

All the while, Bethlehem's inhabitants slept unawares.

[1]Luke 2:25-26

[2]Luke 2:36

[3]Revelation 12:1

[4]The seven great wars of Satan against God: 1) Satan's attempt to dethrone God in eternity past in order to establish himself as the supreme authority, 2) Satan's attack upon God's highest creation, Adam and Eve, 3) Satan's attempt to kill the Christ on the night of his birth, 4) the attempt to kill the child at the age of two by inciting Herod, 5) Satan's assault in Gethsemane where he sought to deter Christ from the cross, 6) the famed coming Battle of Armageddon where Satan will attempt to annihilate Israel, 7) Satan's release after the millennial reign of Christ, when he will rally all who have not bowed to Christ for one final attempt to dethrone God.

[5]Ephesians 6:12

[6]Revelation 12:2

CHAPTER TEN

While Bethlehem Slept

Mary tightly grasped the front of Joseph's robe, drawing him close for comfort. He wrapped her in arms of kindness. Nothing could have prepared them for this night—not even their rich, spiritual heritage. Still, they would have to employ those principles of truth on this battlefield.

"Joseph," she asked, "how can we experience the reality of this evil presence, and yet no one in Bethlehem seems to be aware? What we sense in our spirits is as real as anything we could touch."

Joseph responded in a soothing voice, trying to allay his wife's fears: "I understand. It is amazing how powers in the invisible realm can control events in the visible realm, yet people remain oblivious. Do you remember how Elisha's servant was terrified when the city was surrounded by Arameans? Elisha told the servant not to be afraid, that those who were with them were more than those with the Arameans. It sounded ridiculous to the servant until Elisha prayed for his eyes to be opened and he saw the hills full of horses and chariots of fire encircling them."[1]

Joseph continued, "I wonder what it must be like, right there at the entrance of the cave. Although we are sensing the energy of the battle in our spirits, the mouth of this cave must be choked with God's angels. The shadow of the Almighty must be thick over this place."

"Joseph, who will believe our report? Will anyone ever understand?"

"Few, if any," he responded. "I think we may have to carry this quietly throughout our lives."

Mary cast her eyes toward the cave's entrance and said, "I wonder if we are past the worst of it . . ."

Outside, the two armies were edging closer and closer to the defining moment that would determine which side would win: darkness or light. It was then that Satan's foul promise to his hordes was fulfilled and another sign appeared in heaven: "An enormous red dragon with seven heads and ten horns and seven crowns on his heads. His tail swept a third of the stars out of the sky and flung them to the earth. The dragon stood in front of the woman who was about to give birth, so that he might devour her child the moment it was born."[2]

The sign in heaven was an instant away from manifesting in the war on earth—at the very mouth of the cave. There stood the scarlet dragon before his minions—one third of heaven's former angels—poised to murder the child. He couldn't afford to miss this strategic opportunity to stop God's redemptive plan once and for all. Anticipation among the demons rose to a fevered pitch. Could they win? They had not yet won a single battle against God. Could they do it this time?

Satan yelled violently, "The woman is birthing the child. Our time has come!"

His urgency electrified his devotees. They rushed toward the cave to engage the angels in battle. Ferocious sounds inaudible to human ears echoed throughout the universe: satanic screams, panicked devils, evil cursing—all pressed against God's angelic battle line. Satan's murderous hordes wretchedly attempted to penetrate the cave but were repelled by the holy authority entrusted to the powers of light. The galaxies continued in their orbits, suspended on transparent strings of gravity, deaf and dumb to the horror of the conflict, though they trembled from the rippling shockwaves. Satan ordered repeated surges of evil energy, hoping to either intimidate or fatigue those guarding the tender coming of God in infant form. With grand strength, the white host resisted each attack by forcefully declaring, "The Lord rebuke you!" They were firm and unyielding, speaking with authority backed by power from on high. As they continually declared, "The Lord rebuke you!" the gargantuan wave of darkness was deflected by the host of heaven's shining shields.

Inside, Mary and Joseph felt the storm raging barely an arm's reach away. While God's angels had the power to stop the demons from physically attacking the couple, the angels could not exempt Joseph and Mary from the fury of the struggle. Mary cried out to God as one attempt after another was made to destroy the child starting to emerge from her womb. Joseph knew that if God did not protect them, more than the child would be dead at dawn—they, too, would perish. He thanked the Almighty for his protective shadow.

Mary saw Joseph staring intently into the past, recreating it in the present. His taut lips shaped memories into words: the ones his faith had clung to during the past nine months. Satan was pressing hard to dislodge Joseph's confidence that Mary's pregnancy was from God. Evil thoughts deluged Joseph's mind, pumping horrid emotions into his chest. Joseph fought to recall the day the angel disrupted his bitter hurt, that awful day when it appeared as though Mary had been unfaithful. Fighting the torrent of wickedness and lies fevering his being, he forced out the words of the angel: "Joseph son of David, do not be afraid to take Mary home as your wife, because what is conceived in her is from the Holy Spirit. She will give birth to a son, and you are to give him the name Jesus, because he will save his people from their sins."[3]

The battle for Joseph's mind pressed on. Satan had masterfully spilled the battle into the cave, cleverly attacking Joseph where he was most vulnerable. The months of dark innuendoes and wicked gossip from people back in Nazareth had worn a sore spot on his soul, so the evil one continued suggesting that the child was not conceived by a miraculous act of God. Joseph, grasping his robe, reassured himself that Mary had told him the truth. He rehearsed the words of the angel that he had just quoted. This was his strongest confirmation of Mary's purity. That's where Satan attacked: pressing questions into Joseph's mind that perhaps he had not seen an angel . . . perhaps it was only a dream . . . perhaps it was a demon guised as an angel. Satan was reverting to the question that started Adam's downfall: "Did God really say?" If he could lodge the question, he could bend the man.

When that failed, the devil twisted and turned his lies attempting to incite Joseph. *Fool! Mary was unfaithful to you. This child isn't from God. Fool! You're just a little carpenter! You're a nobody, letting Mary get away with this lie. She's just using you.*

Satan didn't goad Joseph in an audible voice; rather, he imposed dark thoughts, hoping Joseph would believe they were his own. The dragon sought to enrage Joseph to raise his own hand against the unborn child, or against Mary.

Everyone will understand a jilted lover's murderous rage, he hissed into Joseph's mind. But Joseph grew stronger in spirit. He clutched his head, refusing to let the angel's announcement to him in Nazareth be obliterated in the heat of battle. The serpent sank his venomous lies deeper into Joseph's mind, trying to paralyze his confidence. But Joseph stood firm. He repeated the angel's words in heavy, guttural whispers. "Do not be afraid to take Mary home as your wife . . . what is conceived in her is from the Holy Spirit." The harder the devil fought, the more militant became Joseph's determination ". . . what is conceived in her is from the Holy Spirit! Do not be afraid to take Mary home as your wife! Do not be afraid to take Mary home as your wife!"

Frustrated by Joseph's resolve, Satan assailed him from another angle. He awakened vivid memories—white-hot memories—of Joseph's near abandonment of Mary. Joseph felt debilitated, almost immobilized by the accuser's sly tongue: *How could you ever think that Mary . . . pure, wonderful Mary would betray the vows each of you made in your hearts?*

Joseph felt dark, heavy and evil. The scheme nearly worked. For a moment Joseph stopped praying, feeling unworthy of Mary . . . of God . . . of life. He wanted to run, not out of cowardice, but out of a sense of humiliation. The accusation was true. He had nearly rejected his Mary. He had doubted her integrity.

But the devil pushed too far. At last, Joseph looked directly into Mary's eyes seeking forgiveness. Instead, the glow from the flickering fire dancing on her face revealed her need for him to be strong—now! When Joseph saw the cry for help in Mary's eyes, he shook his head violently to dispel the stupor of lies. Suddenly he felt a thousand trumpets renew the call to arms in his soul. He turned his head toward the mouth of the cave, clenched his teeth and declared with clarion-like valor, "What is conceived in her is from the Holy Spirit!"

His faith empowered his voice. His voice empowered the angels. God empowered them all.

Seven miles away at the temple, Simeon continued his vigil, prostrate on the cold stone bench. Sweat dropped from his brow, forming small, dark spots on the sandstone. "O Lord, most faithful God, I cry out to you. Long has Israel suffered from the consequences of her sin. We have violated you, not honoring you with faith, not glorifying you with obedience. O God, O holy one of Israel, hear and listen. Stretch forth your hand and deliver Israel this night."

He paused. The words "this night" had never entered his prayers before. But something within prompted him to pray them. Startled, he prayed on with greater fervor.

Anna was kneeling on the floor, her elbows resting on a square boulder in front of her. The sense of gravity bound her spirit to continue in intense prayer too. "Holy, holy, holy," she repeated. "Most Holy Father, you are strong and mighty. Send your deliverance this night. Forbid your people to suffer further. Do not shame your people as we have shamed you. Be merciful and send your salvation."

The dragon glared toward Jerusalem, his fiery eyes bloated with hate, enraged by the two bright shafts of light rising from the temple all the way to God's throne. He knew it was prayer—a force he had never been able to overcome. If only he could break the shafts and extinguish the prayer, he would have a better chance. He had sent an envoy to intercept their pleas, but the greater the pressure, the harder the intercessors prayed. Simeon and Anna were far too mighty—mighty in faith, mighty in prayer!

The awful, yet wondrous, night wore on. Mary's contractions grew closer together. Satan's opportunity to kill was upon him. He rallied another thunderous, lightning-bolt attack against Joseph, but failed. Joseph's faith held strong, as did heaven's shining host.

Gradually the pitched attacks against Joseph subsided. His heart and mind settled like an ocean-tossed ship entering a haven. He sensed victory was soon at hand.

Finally, the woman in the sky ". . . gave birth to a son, a male child, who will rule all the nations with an iron scepter."[4]

Satan quaked. The Savior-Messiah, the conquering ruler of the world, was born. But now he was in the open and vulnerable. Satan was out of time. Having failed to move Joseph to evil, he was forced to attempt to murder the child himself. He had murdered countless people in the past. Hoping to penetrate the white shield of angels, he planned to enter the cave and devour the child. No thought delighted him more. With not a second to spare, he drew his forces to the height of divine limitation. He rose so high that he could see the sun cresting over the Atlantic. He turned sharply downward, thrusting at the speed of thought, plunging toward the little cave below. A ghastly shriek erupted from his throat as he aimed his javelin-like finger at the child's tiny beating heart.

Joseph was holding the newborn in his hands, tapping on the infant's back to stimulate the child's breathing, when it happened. Satan's army struck with all their might—mustering a force of galactic magnitude. Heaven's angelic host never retreated an inch. They were there under orders of the Almighty. At the split second of impact, they shouted in a mighty voice: "The Lord rebuke you!" The repelling sound ricocheted all the way from Bethlehem to the bottom of hell. The powers of darkness had just collided with the powers of light, and the thunderclap nearly equaled the explosion at creation. It was followed by a few seconds of silence—total, tranquil silence.

Then it came . . . the infant's cry. The delicate, quivering, fragile sound of dependent new life overwhelmed the combined strength of hell.

His cry was heard throughout the universe—a promise to redeem creation itself. Had God permitted, all of creation would have sent sound waves of praise beyond comprehension rumbling throughout space. Creation had been painfully waiting for the Redeemer to set the sons of men free. Only then could the heavens and the earth be whole again. Although the dawn of hope was breaking upon the long cosmic night, God kept the galaxies hushed.

And so Jesus was born on this night, a night clear and calm to the natural eye, but thickly clouded with war in the spirit realm. It was uncanny how alive and active the spirit world was while Bethlehem lay at rest. And the war was vast. Satan had gathered his entire fighting force, attempting to kill the Christ. But the host of heaven had gathered to guard the child's birth, and hell's best effort was broken. The child was born!

And the infant's victorious cry prevailed, while Bethlehem continued its slumber.

[1]2 Kings 6:16-17
[2]Revelation 12:3-4
[3]Matthew 1:20-21
[4]Revelation 12:5

CHAPTER ELEVEN

Moments After the War

Herod could not hear the infant's triumphant cry, but abruptly stopped pacing mid-stride. The messenger of threat pressed his torment deeper: "You're done! Your demise has come! You're finished!"

Herod lifted his face skyward, shook his fist toward the gods and yelled, "No! . . . No! . . . No! I will not be broken! I shall conquer any rival. I shall reign forever!"

He screamed for everyone to leave his presence. Then, with a whimper, he slumped into a chair, alone. His horror-riddled mind reached for a soft, comforting memory, something to ease the fearsome pain. His eyes were glazed as he repeated the name of the wife whom he loved but had murdered. "Miriamne . . . Miriamne, where are you . . . O Miriamne, where are you? Please come to me Miriamne, I need you."

By now the wall guarding his sanity had collapsed completely. He tried to reconstruct it by calling to the past— *Miriamne, Miriamne*—but the wall was forever gone. The past he had destroyed could not save him now.

Dripping with perspiration, he heard the demon's torments. This night the phantom went beyond exciting Herod's thoughts and emotions to confronting him audibly! "Finished! You are destroyed! Tonight is the beginning of the end!"

On the feeding slopes near Bethlehem, the shepherds had experienced their worst night in memory. Relief did not come until deep into the night when the flocks unexplainably settled down. It was as though they heard something that gave them peace. The frenzy calmed, the sheep lowered their ears and laid down.

Satan and his legions broke rank, bloodied and bruised, torn and tired. They returned to their posts around the world to resume their work in the affairs of mankind—ever lurking, hoping for another chance to seize the prize of this eternal conquest.

Heaven's angels remained on the battlefield after the birth, waiting to announce the victory. The shepherds, who were only an earshot from the cave, drowsily discussed the evening's disturbing events as they stared right past the unseen dignitaries gathering before them.

Suddenly, one angel removed the curtain that separates the visible realm from the invisible. Light burst out of the darkened sky, revealing images of beings. It was a wholly different light from that known to earth. It came from within the beings, but cast no shadow on anything around them. There they were—a massive gathering of bright angels surrounded by a star-studded, black universe.

It happened without warning or announcement. Terror gripped the shepherds, and their minds were paralyzed.

Finally, the eternal second eased. An angel spoke: "Do not be afraid. I bring you good news of great joy that will be for all the people. Today in the town of David a Savior has been born to you; he is Christ the Lord. This will be a sign to you: You will find a baby wrapped in cloths and lying in a manger."[1]

There stood the angels, firm and bright, arrayed in the splendor of God's power, declaring the victorious outcome of the war: "A Savior has been born!" Bewildered by the magnitude of the scene, the enormity of this statement eluded the shepherds altogether.

But the angels knew what it meant. This invincible army transformed into a choir, worshipping with one majestic voice: "Glory to God in the highest, and on earth peace to men on whom his favor rests."[2]

The shepherds heard the great sound echoing among the hills, but the angels heard it spreading throughout the universe like a majestic anthem filling the cathedral of the stars. No planet was unaffected. But the glorious praise filled more than the universe; it filled eternity; it filled heaven itself.

Then suddenly it was over. The shepherds gaped into the night sky that seemed blacker and more deeply silent than ever. The stars looked distant, small and dim. The bright light of heaven's presence had exceeded the sun, but they could look directly at it without harming their eyes. Now, as instantaneously as the beings appeared, they were gone. No more explanation was given. The shepherds slowly collected their thoughts and immediately prepared to go to Bethlehem to see the child.

In the cave the fragrance of new life was sweet. Joseph held Mary as she stroked the baby's face. He then rose to run his fingers across the wall of the cave. The gritty sandstone felt as it did before the war—the cave hadn't changed. Yet eternal consequences had been weighed in the balance in this very place. Once the war had ended, it became just a cave again—nothing hallowed, just a place to shelter sheep. It was the event, not the cave, that was hallowed.

The mystery of the unseen world had passed, and the normal realities of the natural world slowly returned. Sometimes

Mary and Joseph felt too warm from the small fire; then soon after, they'd feel a chill wrapping their perspiring bodies. The smell of animals wasn't foreign to them, but the presence of a newborn baby was—a baby whose birth caused heaven and hell to collide.

Raw and ragged from fatigue, they fell asleep, until awakened by a soft cry. The child was hungry. Their hearts stored impressions from the night to be discussed at the appropriate time. This was not the time. The baby was hungry, and that's all that mattered now. After the feeding they fell asleep again, but not for long. The sun was already rising above the wilderness of Samaria, casting a glow across the eastern horizon. A new day was dawning for everyone—indeed for creation as well.

[1]Luke 2:10-12
[2]Luke 2:14

CHAPTER TWELVE

The Day After

Mary and Joseph stirred from their brief, shallow sleep. Unlike the thousands awakening from a restful night, Mary and Joseph were shedding a night that had been steeped in war—a war fought on behalf of those who slept.

The young couple emerged from the most incredible event since time began. The God who created and visited the world in the past had just *entered* it, literally becoming part of it as a human. But that was far too much for Mary and Joseph to think or talk about just now.

A round figure filled the cave's entrance, casting a long shadow across the family. It was the burly owner of the inn. "Shalom!" he boomed, waking the baby who cried—an unsteady, quivering sound. Shocked, the innkeeper raised his thick eyebrows. His eyes darted this way and that, then lit on a small pile of moist, bloody cloths. He lumbered away toward the inn, calling for his wife. Moments later he returned with her as she angrily chattered at him for not asking someone to surrender a room to Mary and Joseph the night before. He explained that he never dreamed Mary was so close to delivery. His reasons sounded artificial and weightless even to him, but Mary assured him she was not angry while Joseph expressed his appreciation for the provision of the cave. Guilt stabbed the large man's heart. "I'll do anything . . . *anything* to help," he earnestly vowed.

"Awful . . . just awful! Big talk! That's all I hear, big talk!" his wife rebuffed, as she stooped to tenderly hand Mary a cool drink. "If you want to help, then go burn those soiled cloths," she instructed. Her wise, maternal manner restored calm to the young couple, giving the assurance that comes when someone enters a new, insecure situation, but knows what to do. Mary felt warmed by thoughts of her own mother far away in Nazareth.

Voices rose and fell just outside the cave, gradually intensifying like an oncoming band. But it had nothing to do with the new parents. The world was rushing into another day as thousands had come to Bethlehem to sign the census commanded by Caesar Augustus. Word was already spreading, however, that an infant was in the cave—born just last night. To most it was no great event—simply another baby. People hurriedly passed the cave to record their names on the census, then begin their arduous trips back home. Some said their morning prayers, not knowing how near God was and what form he had taken.

After arranging a comfortable place for Mary to sit and hold the child, Joseph moved toward the mouth of the cave on his way to add his family to the census. A flashback of the previous night seized his mind, and he stopped dead in his tracks. What would he see outside? After all, a great war had occurred with a clash of energy that could have split Earth in two. Would trees be downed and limbs strewn everywhere? Would broken swords be lying all over the ground? The cave seemed untouched, but what might be outside?

Mary noticed Joseph pause, then watched him exit. He raised his forearm to shield his eyes from the bright sun that gave the sandstone buildings of Bethlehem a golden hue. He squinted, then slowly opened his eyes to assess the damage, but there was none. Everything was just as it had been when they arrived the night before. The trees were swaying gently in the breeze blowing from the desert. There was no evidence of any battle.

Joseph went back into the cave and sat close to Mary, who wondered what he had seen. "Nothing, Mary, there's nothing there. It's just as before," he whispered. The innkeeper's wife continued transforming the cave into a home.

Mary softly responded, "It's a wonder that such an eruption can occur without leaving a trace. There's nothing imaginary about what happened. We felt it in our spirits, even in our bodies, yet it has passed and the world remains the same."

"I know, Mary. It's the same as when the angel appeared to each of us regarding the child's birth: His appearance was so real that it seemed impossible to imagine that other people couldn't see or hear him. Yet, when he departed, life continued as before."

Mary added, "I was amazed last night at how God's authority filled the cave when you were quoting what the angel had said to you. Nothing could undo the Word of God spoken to you."

"Mary, I feel so honored to be your husband, to be with the very woman through whom the Messiah has entered the world. Just think, he's ours to raise . . . for now."

"Yes, Joseph. But I still grieve over those who won't believe us, and the awful things they have said."

"I know, I know." Joseph's voice became subdued. "We should not think about that. God will vindicate us."

"I must go to sign the census now, Mary." He hesitated, looking deeply into her eyes, not wanting to leave her alone—not just yet.

Mary took his face in her hands and, with the respect of Sarah of old, said, "It's all right, my lord, you go. The child and I will be fine." Her voice was firm and assuring.

Joseph marveled at Mary's courage as he bid her goodbye and stepped out of the cave to join the flow of people slowly moving toward the tent where the census was being taken.

Two worlds—the seen and the unseen—were still colliding in Joseph's heart. It wasn't easy to shake off the impact of the spiritual war of the previous night and reenter the everyday world. He had vast questions but set them aside to fulfill his temporal duty. As he walked, he overheard a heated conversation:

"So, what do you think about this census?" asked a man cynically as his straggly beard blew wildly in the breeze.

"While I'm here at this census my family's business is closed, and I'm losing money. Caesar Augustus is doing this just to be sure he gets all the taxes he can, that's what I think," his companion replied angrily.

"Yeah, then they stick Herod over us Jews as our king. He's worse than his father, Antipater—that Edomite dog! And the fact that his father became a proselyte didn't put one drop of Jewish blood in the family's veins," barked a third man, whose bitterness dripped from his lips.

"Worse still, Herod's mother was a Nebatean Arab. So he's born of two Gentile dogs who give him the Greek name Herod," said the first man, glad that his question had unmasked mutual resentment in the group.

A man who puffed on a long, thin pipe joined the conversation. "My parents never could understand why Julius Caesar made Antipater ruler of Palestine."

"I'll never forget the screaming after Julius Caesar's death, when Anthony appointed Herod as our king," added yet another man, dressed in a stately robe.

By now the group was fuming. "Yes, and with Anthony and Octavia fighting for power, they put a Gentile over us to control us with one of their own!"

"There's only one answer," interrupted a soft-spoken gentleman who suddenly emerged in the midst of the throng. "The day is approaching when the Messiah will appear, and soon everything will change."

"Friend, how can you be so sure the Messiah is close at hand?" asked the man with the pipe as he turned to face the stranger. But the gentleman was already gone. He seemed to have materialized then vanished.

Joseph nearly blurted out, "The Messiah is here now!" He actually raised his arm to speak, but stopped cold. It wasn't the time. He knew it was futile to enter the fray with explanations about the previous night. They wouldn't believe him. Besides, he was commissioned to raise the Messiah, not introduce him. Joseph drew his robe more tightly to keep it from flapping in the wind and walked a little faster.

It was almost noon when Joseph stepped into the register's tent. Sitting at a table was a man holding his hand on the parchment that inflated Rome's pride with each additional signature. Joseph looked directly into the man's eyes and proclaimed, "Joseph from Nazareth in Galilee. Family of three: a wife named Mary and a son named Jesus!" It was the first time Joseph had said the name in public. He wasn't sure what to expect. Would the angels begin to sing for joy? Would the demons swirl in fear? Certainly this man would sense the excitement in Joseph's very being and realize that he was face-to-face with the stepfather of the Savior of the world.

The census taker, his mouth down-turned, merely stared ahead blankly. "My family became three only last night," Joseph added with a smile, hoping for a nod of acknowledgment. Instead, the man grunted crudely, his indifference apparent.

Joseph walked out of the tent, leaving behind him the census taker—who would never realize that he had just heard the birth of the Messiah announced.

Shortly after midday Joseph returned to the cave and was surprised to discover several shepherds sitting quietly near Mary and the baby. Mary, smiling as though about to burst, said, "Joseph, these men have something to tell you. You're not going to believe it . . . or, on second thought, I guess you will."

Joseph sat down beside Mary and waited with anticipation. The shepherds gazed upon him, then looked at the baby. Finally, one spoke.

"Well, ah, as we were telling your wife . . ." Insecurity caused a halt in his voice; after all, he was just a shepherd. The magnitude of the predawn announcement from the angel—just hours earlier—was unsettling enough. Now to actually be in the presence of the child declared to be God's "peace on earth" was unnerving. The shepherd felt uneasy viewing Joseph as merely a common carpenter, although his calloused hands revealed his trade.

"Yes, please go on," Joseph said. Now all the shepherds started talking, their words whirling together like swollen streams converging.

"Well, it happened all of a sudden . . ." said the first.

"Yeah, we were all half asleep," said another.

"You wouldn't have believed the light!" exclaimed a third.

"Then I woke up real fast and . . ." started a fourth.

"Wait, wait, hold it," said one in a deep, kind, fatherly tone, who obviously was the leader of the group. "Let me explain what happened, then everyone can fill in the details, okay?" They all agreed.

"Well, sir . . ." he started, when Joseph put up a hand to interrupt.

"Please, just call me Joseph." His voice was quiet and unassuming, devoid of self-importance.

"Well . . . Joseph, what I'm going to tell you may be hard to believe." Joseph smiled, musing how difficult it would be for the shepherds to comprehend what he and Mary had experienced.

"We had a terrible night with the sheep. They kept running in circles and bawling, as though a wolf or lion was near, but there was nothing—no danger at all, at least none that we could see. Still the sheep were nervous, even panicky. We fought hard to herd them each time they scattered." He reenacted the experience with animated expressions.

Then his voice became hushed: "Deep into the night, well before dawn, the sheep finally settled, while some of us were talking. Suddenly a bright light flashed in front of us, and, well . . . well, it was more than a light." He straightened his robe as though to gain courage to continue. "It was . . . it was a gathering of angels!" He paused for dramatic effect.

Joseph's eyes lit up, and he gaped at Mary. "What did the angels say? Please go on," he urged.

"Well, we were terribly frightened. All we could do was stare. We couldn't even speak. In fact I wanted to run, but my legs were locked. We thought we would be killed. But then one of the angels said not to be afraid because he had good news to tell us. He announced that the Christ was born this night in the town of David—you know, right here in Bethlehem—and he gave us a sign to look for. He said we'd find the child wrapped in cloths and lying in a sheep's feeding trough."

A young shepherd interjected, "We didn't want to disturb you too early . . ."

Another added, ". . . so we didn't come until late morning."

Joseph, anxious to return to the topic at hand, asked, "Did the angel say anything else?"

The fatherly shepherd's voice sounded more mystical as he continued, "No, he didn't, but the others—there were too many angels with him to count—they all looked toward heaven and spoke as though in one voice. It was louder than a shout, but sounded melodious. I've never heard anything like it. We could actually feel the praise that flowed from deep within them. They said, 'Glory to God in the highest, and on earth peace to men on whom his favor rests.'[1] That's exactly what they said. I'll never forget those words. I'll never forget the devotion they had toward God."

Another shepherd spoke up, "Hearing the enormous sound they made, well, I just couldn't believe they didn't wake up all of Bethlehem . . ."

"And Jerusalem too!" blurted another.

The moment shifted to Joseph, who said, "There's much more to what happened last night. But I want you men to know how much you have done for Mary and me."

The shepherds looked at one another in wonderment.

"We were told by angels nearly a year ago that Mary was to mother the Christ child," Joseph explained, "and that the birth would be an act of God. We have endured much misunderstanding from people in our hometown. Then, last night, well, that's another story. Let me just say that there was strong resistance to this child's birth. Now, to have you tell us of your experience—the panic of the sheep, the angels' announcement of the child's victorious birth—means more to us than you will ever know. We don't feel so alone. It's a confirmation to us from God himself."

"But why would God show us?" asked one. "We're only shepherds. We don't understand much about these things."

"And why me?" was Joseph's retort. "I'm just a carpenter, not a learned rabbi."

"The greater question is, 'Why me?'" posed Mary. "I'm just a common girl with no special background."

So, there they were, Mary, Joseph and the shepherds, gathered around the Christ child, all feeling both honored and unworthy to be in his presence.

Eventually the shepherds departed for the fields. Their robes billowed in the wind as they descended the slopes from Bethlehem, tapping their crooks with each step. Their hearts were filled with praise to God that they—just simple shepherds—had been included in this divine plan.

By late afternoon the innkeeper and his wife had overheard enough of the conversation between Jesus' parents and the shepherds to be quietly discussing between themselves the marvel of having the Messiah born in their cave. They were consumed with desire to help the couple and the child. With willing hearts, they did.

The innkeeper's wife had spent several hours making the drab shelter as homelike as possible, and by evening it smelled fresh and clean. A fire crackled, bringing warmth to the dank walls of the cave.

"Joseph," said Mary in a way that indicated she wanted to discuss a serious matter. "I don't think we should return to Nazareth. It would not be wise for Jesus to grow up amid the evil whispering of those who do not believe he came from God. Also, Abba says that the prophets wrote that the Messiah is to come from this town."

Joseph nodded. "I agree. It's amazing to think that this One who will sit on King David's throne in Jerusalem will come from Bethlehem—the very town of David's birth. We'll stay. I can do carpentry work here as easily as in Nazareth. I simply need to transfer my tools and our belongings. I'll do that soon. We will stay and raise the child here."

The couple, finally alone with their son, talked no more. They just held each other and the child. As night set in, they all fell into a deep sleep.

[1]Luke 2:14

CHAPTER THIRTEEN

Eight Days Later

The thick, heavy temple walls at Jerusalem had not yet warmed in the morning glow. A priest stepped into the temple out of the brightness of the arching sun, rubbing his shoulders as his body rippled from the invigorating chill lingering from the night before. Whispers resonated from wall to wall, and the sound of shuffling feet could be heard as priests scurried about. There was no anticipation that this would be anything but just another day: the smell of burnt offerings and rising incense, the settling of disputes, the selling of sacrificial birds and animals, the repetitious drone of prayers.

But this day would prove different from all the rest. The God of the temple—whose presence slew any high priest who entered the holy of holies without proper cleansing—was being brought into the temple in a most humble fashion. No one expected to meet God this way, although Isaiah had predicted it. There, slowly climbing one step after another, came Mary and Joseph carrying the Messiah in their arms. It was time to circumcise and officially name the child. He was eight days old.

Unpretentious, they made their way into the outer court in search of a priest, barely noticed except by that unique pair whose presence had become part of temple life. Mary and Joseph with the baby were about to pass by Simeon. Anna was standing at a distance, but both had the same inner witness that this was the one for whose coming and protection they had prayed.

Anna and Simeon were not bound in marriage, but indeed bound in ministry. Their eyes were fastened on Mary and Joseph who were cradling Immanuel himself! Simeon and Anna glanced at each other knowingly from across the courtyard, then back at the approaching family. They understood this was not just another Jewish infant.

Simeon quietly intercepted Mary and Joseph. They knew of his reputation—the man who gave his life to praying for the Messiah. Without word or hesitation, they placed the child in Simeon's outstretched arms.

Drawing the priceless treasure to his chest, Simeon looked deeply into the infant's face for the longest time. He pondered the mighty sovereign plan that lay enfolded within the soft skin of the child.

Silence. Silence filled with music in his soul. His heart enlarged beyond measure to think of who was in his arms. He seemed oblivious of Mary and Joseph, nor did they seek attention. He was worshipping *their* child, and they knew it. They had handed their entrustment to Simeon, sensing that he was as much a part of God's plan for the child as they. This was the great intercessor, who, along with Anna, prayed the Messiah safely onto earth.

After a long pause, Simeon took a deep breath and raised the child high toward heaven—a pose of triumph and praise. Indeed, the armies of the Most High had prevailed, and the child had overcome the vicious assault of hell. The Messiah in infant form was alive and well on earth. Simeon, who had fought many battles in prayer for the coming of this child, could contain his heart no more. Lifting up the One before whom every knee would someday bow, he joyfully declared, "Sovereign Lord, as you have promised, you now dismiss your servant in peace. For my eyes have seen your salvation, which you have prepared in the sight of all people, a light for revelation to the Gentiles and for glory to your people Israel."[1]

An inaudible but horrible shriek went up as Satan and his hordes watched helplessly from the distant Judean hills. He paced and snarled, hatred dripping from his pores and rage coursing through his heart. Hopelessly trapped within himself, he determined that he would dog this child throughout his life, committing to kill him before the cross. Satan was aware of the coming cross and what it meant. He had listened carefully to the prophets of old. He knew that if this one could endure a sinless life and remain obedient to the Father all the way to the crucifixion, then Satan's head would be crushed[2]; he would be stripped of all authority over mankind, and he would have to surrender the keys of death. He was appalled to see the child raised up in triumph, a sure sign that he—Satan—had lost again.

Simeon slowly lowered the child, then turned to Mary and Joseph. In solemn tones he said, "This child is destined to cause the falling and rising of many in Israel, and to be a sign that will be spoken against, so that the thoughts of many hearts will be revealed. And a sword will pierce your own soul too."[3]

Mary and Joseph were sobered but not frightened by the prophetic words. Instead, they clasped hands in resolve. The war of the universe had fallen upon their son and they would feel the fallout.

By now Anna had drawn near, watching and listening to the words of Simeon. Suddenly she burst into praise! "Hallelujah! Glory to God on high, who has fulfilled his promise to Israel."

A small crowd was gathering, among them some priests. Anna turned to those who had looked forward to the coming Messiah and said, "This is the one of whom the prophets spoke.

This is the Son of the living God who has come to bring the redemption of Jerusalem."[4]

Speechless. Everyone was speechless. The small group stood staring at the child. Believing priests raised their arms to God. Skeptics turned and walked away, saying nothing. The silence was shattered when one priest said, "It's time to circumcise the child. What will his name be?"

"Jesus," answered Joseph.

Simeon and Anna stepped alone to a section of the outer court. Simeon spoke, "This certainly explains the horrific battle we experienced in prayer just eight nights ago." Both were still recovering from the awful strain.

"Indeed," Anna replied. "I was always certain of the promise that we'd see the child, but the reality far exceeds my expectations. This is such a holy day for Israel, yet the world goes on in mundane affairs."

Simeon took Anna's hand. "Anna, you have been so faithful to God. I honor you."

"Many days I drew new courage, Simeon, when I saw you enter the temple. Thank you for your unwavering commitment."

After a long moment of quietude and mutual admiration, their hands slipped apart. Simeon departed the temple as a soldier laying down his arms after his final great victory. He went to put his affairs in order and prepared to meet the God he had so fervently served. Anna melted into the temple life, continuing to worship and pray for her few days that remained. Two mighty prayer warriors—weak in age, but steadfast in spirit, unconquerable by the hordes of hell—parted to lay their victory before the throne of God.

[1]Luke 2:29-32
[2]Genesis 3:15
[3]Luke 2:34-35
[4]Luke 2:36-38

CHAPTER FOURTEEN

Two Years Later

Over the next two years talk spread among the common people about the child born in a cave, especially the claims that he was the prophesied King of the Jews—born right here in Bethlehem. The shepherds' candid account seemed credible to most. The stories remained underground, however, since no one wanted to risk the wrath of Caesar Augustus in Rome or Herod the Great in Jerusalem. They knew that the birth of a world-conquering king would not be met with favor.

The rabbis who heard the story smiled condescendingly, assuring the people that there was no reason to put much credence in it, since many others had also claimed to be the Messiah. Besides, they reasoned, the real Messiah would come as a great man, riding a horse—not as a squalling infant in a cave. Centuries of unbelief had tightened the blindfold covering their eyes, so that clearly-stated prophecy could not be grasped by them.

Thus, the truth remained shielded from the proud and mighty, those too filled with worldly wisdom to believe and bow. To them the ways of God appeared foolish.

Joseph and Mary lived in a small home. Joseph worked his trade, and Mary raised the child. They developed friendships in the town as a result of their active participation in the synagogue. They planned to remain there, at least until Jesus was grown, then they would decide whether to make Bethlehem their permanent home, or return to Nazareth.

On one particular day an unusual event caused a great stir in the city of Jerusalem. A young lad ran through the Sheep Gate and into the city, his nimble legs propelling him forward and his skinny arms whirling in every direction. Juvenile excitement drove his voice to a high pitch as he exclaimed, "Look! Look! . . . Look at the Magi!" as though officially sent to announce their arrival. Lumbering through the gate was a small caravan with camels gargling and groaning, disgruntled by the commotion. Their feet had not flattened on a stone-bed road since they departed their distant city.

Rocking back and forth, sitting high on the camels' backs, were stately men draped in Oriental prestige: purple robes, white satin turbans, gold neck chains, rare stone rings. They looked straight ahead, comfortable and confident. An entourage of guards and servants rode other camels, looking drab in comparison to the Magi.

Shepherds were gathered at the gate, bartering sheep for temple sacrifices as well as household needs. They tilted their heads upward, shielded their eyes from the sun, squinted and watched the parade.

All became quiet as the caravan passed. The Magi were impressive, but unknown.

"Which way to the palace?" one called to the shepherds below.

"Straight ahead. You'll easily find it to the north of the temple," one responded.

Slowly the waggling procession was swallowed by the city.

In the palace an aide pounded on the thick wooden door that opened to Herod's quarters.

"Enter!" Herod boomed.

Having learned to bow low in high places, the fidgety assistant swooped so as not to lose Herod's favor.

"Your majesty," said the aide, "there are some men who wish to see you. They are not on your schedule, but they just arrived from the East. I would not disturb you with this matter, but they appear very important—certainly not as important as you—but important. They say they only want to ask you about a child who has been born King of the Jews." Blood drained from the messenger's head, knowing such a statement could enrage the king.

Herod stared at the wall behind his assistant, seemingly unruffled, but a caldron of fear and fury boiled in his heart. The tormentor stirred within, reminding him of the vicious warnings he had received two years earlier. Herod waited for his neck to stop pulsating, then, flipping his hand to show indifference, he said, "I'm very busy. Give me some time. Then I will see them."

The aide departed. Herod—about to vomit, his body shaking violently—rushed to the balcony both to breathe and establish his plan. He feared that the end was nigh, yet he was impassioned never to be replaced. Spreading his arms, he pressed his palms down on the sandstone ledge, leaned heavily and thought.

More than Herod's resident spirit was present; Satan—the dragon himself—raced to the palace. This was Satan's second grand opportunity to destroy the only One who could deliver mankind from his deadly grasp. He breathed hotly upon the back of Herod's neck. *Kill the child, kill him,* he snarled. Herod felt a murderous urge rising up within his breast. His arrogance was akin to the dragon, making him vulnerable to fulfill the dragon's wish.

The devilish plan that found rich nourishment in Herod's dementia flooded to the surface. *If I kill this infant king,* he thought, *then I can gain immortality and secure my position forever.*

Yes . . . yes . . . I can be the eternal king of the Jews. This madness made sense to his madness. The unseen resident of his soul gave assurance. The dragon nodded approvingly.

Now braced, he shoved himself back from the ledge, took a deep breath, donned a smile and opened the chamber door. There waited the regal visitors.

"Please, please enter." Herod tipped his head slightly to give scant honor to their rank. They, in return, bowed deeply as they walked past him and entered the room. Herod shut the door to emphasize the importance he attached to their presence. When he turned to face them, they held out gifts—a common Oriental practice. He received them and assured the Magi that they were most welcome to enjoy the finest his kingdom offered.

"What is the purpose of your visit to my domain?" he inquired.

One stepped forward and spoke in a deep, stately manner, "Where is the one who has been born king of the Jews? We saw his star in the east and have come to worship him."[1] The wise men saw no reason for this request to threaten Herod, since he had gained the throne at the age of thirty-six and was now in his late sixties.

The muscles in Herod's face rippled as though he were grinding sand in his teeth, but he guised his agitation to appear as concern for the child.

"I, too, want to know," he said. "I will ask my seers and will send for you as soon as I discover the truth."

They departed. Herod stood firmly planted until they were out of earshot, then slammed his fist on a heavy wooden table. Calling his council together and yelling at the top of his voice, he demanded information about a new king. No one knew a thing. All were troubled, since they feared for their lives should Herod hold them accountable for their ignorance. It was their job to protect his throne.

After dismissing his counselors, he called his aide. "Get every chief priest and teacher of the law in this city to the palace—now!" he demanded, his voice echoing throughout the halls.

Robes ruffled as the Jewish leaders scurried through the streets of Jerusalem to the palace. They hated Herod, but knew not to agitate this man who would murder in an instant to protect his throne.

Finally, they assembled in Herod's chamber. Eyes shifted to one another, but no one dared to look directly at the king. Herod's acrid voice eventually shattered the uneasy calm. "Where is the Christ supposed to be born?" he demanded. It was clear that he thought they had been hiding something from him.

Their words dripped with innocence as they responded, "Bethlehem in Judah, as is stated in the writings of the prophet Micah."

One rabbi quoted the prophecy from memory: "But you, Bethlehem, in the land of Judah, are by no means least among the rulers of Judah; for out of you will come a ruler who will be the shepherd of my people Israel."[2]

A gaping silence followed.

Then in a sullen tone Herod said, "Leave. All of you, leave my presence now."

He seethed through clenched teeth, "How can this be? How can this child who wants my throne be growing up just a few miles from here?"

He stewed about his plot to murder the child but knew he could not tell anyone. His position had always been precarious. His Gentile past and wicked ways had long been salt in the Jewish wound. Paranoia had driven him to build safe places of escape, such as Masada and the Herodian. Assassination attempts had been made against him, and twice he had attempted suicide.

Insecure, desperate, he scoured his mind for a solution. Finally it came . . .

[1]Matthew 2:2
[2]Matthew 2:6

CHAPTER FIFTEEN

The Evil Plot

Near midnight Herod sent his aide to awaken the Magi and secretly escort them to his chamber. The assistant was instructed to tell them that he had information of great importance, so that they would not suspect his plot. The moon was full and rich in the sky as the eastern visitors, stirred with interest, rushed to the palace.

Herod stood on the balcony, rocking on his feet, rubbing his beard . . . hoping the Magi would not be seen coming to his throne room. No one must discover how he would find the child, nor that he would arrange the child's death.

Soon the distinguished group arrived in the king's chamber—sleepy, but intrigued. Herod sounded mellow and spiritual as he spoke. "When did you first see the star?" he questioned.

"Two years ago," was the reply.

Herod thought his heart would stop. A chill rippled through his body as the words of the Magi echoed in his ears, confirming the threats of his tormentor on that dreadful night.

"Ah," he said, with slow, masterful control. "This is good. How long we have waited for this One to come. And I have learned where he lives. He is in Bethlehem, only seven miles away. Isn't it amazing that he is so close, yet we were not aware?"

"I'm deeply concerned for the child's safety," he continued, surprising himself with his ability to feign sympathetic camaraderie. "You know that there are others claiming to be the Christ. One of them may harm or even kill the child." He lifted his hand in a benevolent gesture.

Having cleverly woven a bond with the Magi, Herod now set forth his devious plan. "Please, leave quietly for Bethlehem this very night—before dawn. That way no one will see you. 'Go and make a careful search for the child. As soon as you find him, report to me, so that I too may go and worship him.'"[1]

Smiles of agreement were exchanged, and sounds of approval filled the air. They sealed their pact as though all were keepers of the divine gift. The rulers left the palace to rouse their servants, and then departed for Bethlehem.

No sooner were the Magi out of the palace when Herod spun in circles, arms raised and robe flaring to the sides. His whole body was alive with glee. He wrote a prose about his own greatness, then put it to tune:

"I built the Temple for the Jews—

"a gift so rare, they couldn't refuse.

"They will call me King of kings.

"Forever and ever, they'll honor my ruse."

He went out on the balcony, looked toward the sky and smiled smugly, certain that he had finally outwitted the gods— especially the God of the Jews.

The dragon grinned and applauded heartily.

It took most of the remaining night for the Magi to move their sluggish entourage, but they finally settled near a well on the slopes of the shepherds' fields, about a mile from Bethlehem. The next morning, they decided to enter the town without attracting attention, shedding their royal robes for the coarse brown garments of their servants. Traveling on foot, they bade the guards and servants to remain at the well with the camels. They entered Bethlehem looking like a straggly nomadic group that was simply passing through the area—all the while believing that they were involved in a vital plan for the child's safety.

They soon learned that the child had been born in a cave owned by an innkeeper. So, finding the short, rotund man, they convinced him of their intent. It wasn't easy at first, since they looked so motley. When they showed him the gifts they wanted to present, however, he knew such largess couldn't come from mere traders, so he told them where Mary and Joseph lived.

The pomp and poise of the Magi dissipated as they prepared to knock on the door of the small sandstone home that housed the young Prince of Peace. What gave them pause before knocking was the appearance of the door—it was carved so ornately: with sheep, birds and vines with clusters of grapes.

The thick wooden door hung on crude metal hinges, locked with a sliding wood board. A piece of leather served as the handle. Feeling awkward and insecure, the Magi finally knocked. It was easy for them to be in the presence of Herod's pompous pretense, but now they were about to step into the presence of sovereign royalty. They stood in reverential silence.

As Mary opened the door to the unimpressive dwelling, the Magi's eyes grew wide, as though peering into the gates of heaven. For the first time in their lives they were beyond their comfort. They had learned never to speak the name of God— even in a whisper. Now, they were about to see Immanuel: God with us. How should they address him? What would he be like? Did they have a right to be here?

They all felt the magnitude of this hallowed moment.

"What can your servant do for you?" Mary asked. The contrast between the sacred and the profane was instantly clear. They had to bow before Herod, but the mother of the Messiah identified herself as their servant. Joseph stepped to the door behind Mary.

One of the men spoke for the group, "Please forgive our appearance. We are actually Magi from afar. We met with Herod on our way here, and he expressed concern lest some false messiah would try to harm the child. We left our caravan on the shepherds' fields and put on servant clothes so as not to draw attention to our visit."

Joseph cocked his head, surprised to think that Herod would be sympathetic. He had no difficulty, however, believing that these men were genuine Magi, since the one who spoke did so with flawless diction and commanding elocution.

The spokesman continued: "We saw a new star appear in the eastern sky and became convinced that this was a sign that the King of the Jews had been born."

"When did you see this star?" questioned Joseph.

"Two years ago," responded another in the group. "It took this long for us to arrange our affairs and make the journey."

"I understand," replied Joseph. "Please come in." He and Mary stepped back to allow their entrance. Mary immediately gave them a refreshing drink.

Then the moment came . . .

They had traveled very far, and now years of anticipation drew to a close. Little Jesus walked into the room: a normal two-year old, walking awkwardly, speaking only a few words, captivated in a child's world of thought. Joseph lifted Jesus into his arms, and Mary tousled her son's hair.

At first it seemed strange to see Immanuel in this state, but then the Magi marveled to think that God had chosen to endure the full range of the human life, starting at the cradle itself. How else would he enter the world except through the natural process of the highest of all creation? He would not only have to go to the bottom of hell to lift mankind on high, he also had to enter the simplest level of human experience in order to exalt the redeemed to a world infinitely beyond this one. Here was the child upon whose shoulders heaven would eventually hang the governments of the world.

The Magi fell to their knees and bowed before him, worshipping and praising God, and clearly exalting the child as divine. They understood the Scriptures well enough to know that it would be idolatry to bow to a mere mortal in like fashion. This was the moment, however, for deep, humble reverence.

After a long period of worship, they slowly rose and gave three prophetic gifts to the child: gold in honor of his coming reign upon David's throne, incense in honor of his high priesthood and myrrh in honor of his coming sacrifice as Savior of the world.

Late that afternoon they departed for their encampment—pensive, deeply contemplative, each savoring the experience. Finally one broke the silence. "I am glad we wore common clothes. The Messiah came to us in a humble dwelling and in the form of a child. I would not have been comfortable wearing royal robes."

A hum of agreement was heard. Then they continued on in silence, the silence of completeness.

The next morning, as the Magi sat near the fire eating breakfast, one spoke, "I had a disturbing dream last night. I am sure it was a divine message—every bit as sure as we were that the star was a sign of the Messiah's birth."

"Before you speak further," said a second, "let me tell you my dream to see if they are alike. I dreamed of someone—I believe it was an angel—warning us not to go back and tell Herod where to find the child."

"Yes! Yes, that was my dream exactly!" exclaimed the first.

The third spoke, "And it has been confirmed threefold. I, too, had the identical dream."

That day, they did not go northeast to Jerusalem; instead, they avoided the city by taking another route back to their region.

The Magi were not the only ones dreaming. Later that night Joseph had a dream too. An angel appeared to him saying: "Get up, take the child and his mother and escape to Egypt. Stay there until I tell you, for Herod is going to search for the child to kill him."[2]

Mary and Joseph departed immediately, carrying no more than the supplies needed for the journey and Joseph's tools of trade.

"Look, Joseph," Mary said pointing back to their little home. She needed to say no more as Joseph glanced over his shoulder. Remaining behind was the ornate door that held so many memories: the expression of their early love, nearly lost, then restored unto a purpose beyond themselves. Joseph cleared his throat and brushed his eye with the back of his hand. Then they turned toward Egypt, leaving Bethlehem behind.

By going to Egypt, another phase of prophecy would be fulfilled. The Messiah was to be born in Bethlehem, then protected in Egypt—a beautiful expression by God that the child came to save the whole world, not just the Jews.

Eventually Herod grew restless, wondering why the Magi had not returned. He sent a spy to Bethlehem to find them. The spy, not knowing to inquire about nomads in rugged attire, asked for the house where the royally-dressed Magi had visited. He gave the exact number of the members in the entourage, including the soldiers and servants. No one was found who had seen such a caravan as he described.

Desperate for information that would appease Herod's wrath, the spy even went from door-to-door in parts of the village. Surely someone had seen the regal group. At day's end, he came upon a curious sight: an ornately carved door hung open at the entrance of an empty house. "Why would someone leave such a beautiful piece of work behind?" he wondered aloud. The spy paused for only a moment, not taking the time to answer his own question. He needed to return to the palace.

The king had sent word demanding a report, and he would not be pleased.

King Herod ripped his robe in a frenzied rage. He knew he had been outwitted. By asking the wrong questions, the spy had failed to learn that Mary, Joseph and Jesus were on their way to Egypt. He assumed they were still somewhere in Bethlehem. The spy feared for his life, but was abruptly dismissed.

Herod screamed for the commander of his army who arrived to find the king infuriated. In his breast was the panicked demon. Behind him was the livid dragon. Herod drew his sword, pointed it at his commander and roared, "Kill every male child up to two years of age in Bethlehem and the surrounding area! Now! Do it now! I have learned of a plot to overthrow this government, and it must be stopped!"

The commander stood dazed. Numb. Motionless.

"Now!" screamed Herod, "Now!" and threw his sword across the floor.

Herod, the demon and the dragon were frustrated.

The commander prepared a large group of soldiers, who were about to unwittingly fulfill the prophecy: "A voice is heard in Ramah, mourning and great weeping, Rachel weeping for her children and refusing to be comforted, because her children are no more."[3]

It happened in the still of the morning of the following day. Herod's evil had brewed and boiled over, sending a storm of death on horseback to Bethlehem.

Mothers greeted the day with dreams and hope—committed to prepare their children for life. Suddenly, the tranquil dawn was shattered by a fearsome pounding on the door of a Jewish home. The commander pounded with a vengeance, swallowing hard to suppress his nausea. He, too, had children of his own. Timorously, a young woman opened

the door of the first home. "Bring your boy child!" he demanded. This day was the child's second birthday—a cause for joy.
She rushed to get her son, certain that quick submission would
bring favor. When she returned with the boy, the soldier dangled
him high by one arm and began the vulgar massacre. The
soldiers mounted nearby looked away.

The commander dropped the lifeless body at his mother's
feet. She clutched her baby to her breast, soaking her garment
with his blood, and rocked back and forth as though trying to
put her life into him. The sounds she evoked out of shock and
anguish were ghastly.

Other soldiers had scattered to the perimeters of the
town to work inward, so that the wail of horror would not
alert families to hide in the shepherds' caves or escape into the
Judean wilderness. Throughout the morning, the brutal wave
of horror spread until the whole town was a fresh, open grave
of grief. Fathers felt emasculated as they watched their sons
being slaughtered. Some, compelled to defend their families,
flung themselves into the fray, but they, too, were slain.

All of the soldiers held a copy of the census taken by
Caesar Augustus two years earlier. They knew exactly which
homes harbored little boys, and they made sure that no male
children up to two years of age survived that day. By nightfall,
Bethlehem had become the killing fields of the innocents—
drenched in the mad carnage of Herod's impassioned desire to
murder the coming King of the Jews.

And so the dragon, riding on Herod's demented hate and
thirst for eternal power, failed in his second attempt to kill the
Savior of the world. Jesus and his parents were a diminishing dot
on the desert landscape, moving southward to Egypt. Here the
three remained, shielded by obscurity until Herod's death. At
that time, an angel spoke to Joseph in a dream:

"Get up, take the child and his mother and go to the land of Israel, for those who were trying to take the child's life are dead." So he got up, took the child and his mother and went to the land of Israel. But when he heard that Archelaus was reigning in Judea in place of his father Herod, he was afraid to go there. Having been warned in a dream, he withdrew to the district of Galilee, and he went and lived in a town called Nazareth. So was fulfilled what was said through the prophets: "He will be called a Nazarene."[4]

Jesus was over four years of age when Herod the Great died. Mary and Joseph were surprised to be directed back to Nazareth, the village they never expected to see again. They had allowed personal dreams to die in order to raise the Savior of life. Now they returned home, only to find the people divided over the child: some lavishing love and respect, others rejecting the family as outcasts. Evil rumors had etched dark grooves in people's minds over the years.

The young couple had been radically changed by the impact of the previous years' happenings, and they were different upon their arrival home—weathered in wisdom. Though they were back in Nazareth, they were forever enlarged, and could never be the same again. Their vision and sense of destiny extended far beyond Nazareth and the Valley of Jezreel.

The townspeople had honored Joseph enough not to have disturbed his carpentry shop during the time he was away, and soon he resumed his daily routine: hammering, shaping, creating; crafting beds, tables, doors . . .

Doors. On this day he was carving a new door for his Mary—one with sheep, birds and vines with clusters of grapes. A shadow fell across his work. He looked up to see Jesus standing in the open doorway.

"Jesus, my boy," he said with fatherly warmth. Jesus ran to him laughing. Mary entered immediately after, carrying warm bread and cool water for Joseph. The fragrance of fresh baked dough flooded the room completely. She spread a cloth on the worktable and placed the bread on it. After offering thanks, Joseph took a large bite. It was soft and satisfying.

Mary stood close to Joseph as Jesus ran his hand over the intricate carvings on the door. "He's been asking big questions again today," Mary said. Children often ask questions about life, death and forever. But Jesus also asked questions about the Law and the sacrifices. Though God, he had to learn as people do.

Jesus walked quietly around the shop, drinking in his father's work. Mary and Joseph were talking softly when they noticed him staring at a door leaning against the wall in the corner. It was badly gashed, and protruding above the deep scars was a cross—a full, man-sized cross.

Young Jesus touched the cross and felt something stir within.

[1]Matthew 2:8
[2]Matthew 3:13
[3]Jeremiah 31:15
[4]Matthew 2:19-23

From That Time Until Now

In the years to follow . . .

Mary's parents probably lived out their lives in Nazareth, facing the stigma placed on their family by those who doubted the origin of Mary's child. The controversy over their grandson took on epic proportions when, years later, he returned to his home town, stood in the synagogue and claimed to be the one of whom Isaiah had prophesied. The crowd tried to kill him.[1]

Elizabeth and Zechariah were probably not alive to see their son beheaded, since they were quite aged when he was born. However, they remain examples of God's miraculous work and his faithfulness in answering prayer.[2]

John the Baptist, the forerunner of Jesus Christ, went on to call people to repent and turn to God for salvation. Once Christ appeared in a crowd where John was speaking. He pointed to the Lord and announced: "Look, the Lamb of God, who takes away the sin of the world!"[3]

John was beheaded by King Herod (a descendant of King Herod the Great, who died while Christ was a child in Egypt) at the request of Salome, the daughter of a woman who hated John for condemning her adulterous marriage to Herod. While John was in prison, Jesus proclaimed, "I tell you the truth: Among those born of women there has not risen anyone greater than John the Baptist."[4]

King Herod the Great, known for his manipulative and murderous ways, died an ignoble death, his mind scrambled by insanity, his body decaying from abuse. While he was famed for building grand edifices, he was equally famed as the destroyer of lives. His most notorious crime is etched on the wall of eternity—the numerous children he commanded to be murdered in his savage attack against the young King of the Jews.

The innkeeper and his wife were not specifically mentioned in Scripture. Regardless, God orchestrated the necessary people and plans so that Mary ". . . gave birth to her firstborn, a son . . . and placed him in a manger, because there was no room for them in the inn."[5]

The shepherds, who were such a grand encouragement to Mary and Joseph the day after the night of holy war, disappeared from the pages of history. Their children, who were raised hearing the story of the angelic appearance, may have become some of Christ's followers more than thirty years later.

The Magi returned to their region and were never again spoken of in history, though they are remembered for the faith that carried them many miles to worship the prophesied King.

Simeon probably never changed his discipline of prayer, but only changed its emphasis from petition to praise. We do not know how long he lived after seeing the promised Messiah. His story goes silent.

Anna likewise has her life's story hushed after her encounter with the eight-day-old Messiah, but surely spent the remainder of her days in the serenity of the knowledge that she had beheld with her own eyes the promised Son of God.

Mary and Joseph raised Jesus, then became his followers. Joseph may have died early in life, since we have no account of him after Jesus was in the temple as a boy. Mary had to draw on every bit of faith and natural strength she possessed to watch her son become the Man of Sorrows, despised, rejected, then crucified.

The unspeakable joy she experienced the day Gabriel announced that she was to be the Messiah's mother would not be experienced again until she saw Jesus as the conquering Savior after his resurrection. Of all the many ways sinners have been used by God, Mary holds the most unique position. Truly she was blessed of God.

The dragon and his hordes prepared for their future wars against the Christ. Satan would attack Jesus in the desert, offering three temptations to end his suffering. He assaulted him again in the Garden of Gethsemane and on the cross, trying to stop the sacrifice for sin from being made.

For the past two thousand years Satan has been opposing the advance of the gospel of Jesus Christ by resisting and attacking the Church. Today he is preparing to take over the world as the Antichrist, but will be defeated at the Battle of Armageddon.[6] He will be chained in the pit for one thousand years, then allowed to sift the nations once again. This will bring about his final defeat, after which he and his followers, both demonic and human, will be thrown into the lake of fire forever.[7]

Gabriel and the heavenly host ascended on high to await future orders from the throne of God. Michael, the archangel who assisted Gabriel in breaking through to Daniel, will be the one to shout at the next coming of Christ. It is also known that some of the angels of God are worshipping around God's throne, while others are actively involved in the lives of God's people to this day—mostly unawares.

Jesus Christ, the child born on this silent night amid a holy war, went on to become the sacrificial Lamb to pay for the sins of the world. Three days after his crucifixion he was raised again to life, appeared to more than five hundred people over a six week period, gave final instructions to his disciples, entrusted the furtherance of his work to the Holy Spirit, then ascended on high to be seated as the King of Kings and Lord of Lords. His followers have anticipated a soon coming time when he will call his children unto himself, return for the Battle of Armageddon, then set up the kingdom of God on earth.

While the apostle John was imprisoned on the island of Patmos, he was lifted from his cell into the presence of Christ on high. He described the honor being bestowed upon this one who destroyed the works of the devil, broke the power of sin and took away the sin of the world, thereby providing salvation for allwho will call upon his name. John wrote:

> Whenever the living creatures give glory, honor and thanks to him who sits on the throne and who lives for ever and ever, the twenty-four elders fall down before him who sits on the throne, and worship him who lives for ever and ever. They lay their crowns before the throne and say: "You are worthy, our Lord and God, to receive glory and honor and power, for you created all things, and by your will they were created and have their being."[8]

> "Worthy is the Lamb, who was slain, to receive power and wealth and wisdom and strength and honor and glory and praise! To him who sits on the throne and to the Lamb be praise and honor and glory and power, for ever and ever!"[9]

You! . . . what about you? Where do you fit into this ongoing, eternal story? You have seen the varied responses to Jesus Christ while he was on earth. The same array of responses continues to this day. It was for you that Christ entered the world in infant form on that silent night of holy war. Some day soon you will be called to give an account of how you responded to the Son of God. You will be judged according to how you judged him.

Here is a prayer for you to use, whether you are placing faith in Christ for the first time in your life, or you are a long-standing believer who feels moved to make a deeper commitment:

Dear Heavenly Father, based upon the death and resurrection of Jesus Christ, I am trusting your forgiveness for all my sins. I'm asking you to give me the power to live daily for you, growing in my commitment to your Son and fulfilling your will from now, until I meet you in heaven.

I pray in Jesus' name, Amen.

[1]Luke 4:14-30
[2]Luke 1:13
[3]John 1:29
[4]Matthew 11:11
[5]Luke 2:7
[6]Revelation 16:16
[7]Revelation 20:7-10
[8]Revelation 4:9-11
[9]Revelation 5:12-13

An Interview
with Ron Susek

**Golden Quill speaks with the author of *Holding Nothing
Back*, the intriguing story of a one-time Hitler youth
who became a missionary statesman.**

GQ: Knowing that stories of people's lives don't sell unless
they are famous or infamous, what caused you to write
about Ernst Vatter's life?

RS: Dr. Vatter and I were co-speakers at a pastors'
conference in Micronesia. One day at lunch I was asking
him questions about his life, just to get to know him. Two
hours later my eyes were bulging with amazement, not
only by what he endured but how he overcame it.

GQ: What made his story stand out from so many others?

RS: I once read that a story about someone's life is useless
if it doesn't enlarge the soul of the reader. While many
stories are dramatic—as this one is—they don't all enlarge the
soul. Thrilling the reader and giving them insights that
enable them to live greater lives are two different things.
This story does both.

GQ: What distinguishes this story from the many rising out
of the World War II era?

RS: I know of few, if any, stories of a German teenage boy
illegally arrested, experiencing horrors that could have
negatively affected him for life, only to emerge with a
conversion to Christ and a life of rare impact for God. I still
find elements of his life shaping mine.

GQ: Was there a defining moment that caused you to feel this story needed to be told?

RS: Yes. Early on I said, "Ernst, I will consider writing your story only if you will take me into the inside of you and give me a true picture of the good and the ugly. I don't like falsified stories that put halos atop the main character's head. That's both unattainable to the reader and a deception in the story." He laughed and said he'd let me know the real Ernst. And that he did.

GQ: How do you hope Ernst's story will affect people?

RS: I think it's an eye opener to people old enough to remember WWII. There are many insights that will prove invaluable as we trace how Ernst grappled with the battles of his own heart. The book carries major life challenges for young people. If I had a son or daughter, this book would be must reading.

GQ: You went to Germany to research the story. Why?

RS: I had to see, hear, smell, taste and touch Ernst's world in order to bring it alive in the senses of the reader.

GQ: Of all the insights into life found in story, which one impresses you the most?

RS: The way Ernst proved God over and over. He was a man with gaping flaws, but a man who held nothing back from God and God held nothing back from him.

An excerpt from Ron Susek's riveting account of a former Nazi youth turned missionary statesman

Holding Nothing Back

Ernst Vatter: Portrait of Perseverance

BY RON SUSEK

Golden Quill
PUBLISHING
Gettysburg, Pennsylvania

CHAPTER SIX

Life in the Evil Abyss

Ernst recognized some villagers among the prisoners but gained no comfort from their presence. There was no camaraderie; he was younger than the rest and had not been in the military. While he had seen the aftermath of the bombings, he had never stared down the barrel of an enemy gun. These prisoners bore a hardness that came from the trenches of combat.

"Look, kid," one said, "don't be scared. We'll make it." Ernst nodded, then looked back to the valley that cradled his home.

The truck bounded and rumbled northward for an hour until it stopped in Tuebingen where it was met by soldiers with guns raised. "Get down! Get down!" came the order. Ernst jumped off the truck and saw a massive building surrounded by a steel fence to his right. It was a German barracks. "March into that building!" was the next command. The very building that had been home to some of Hitler's troops was now their prison, at least for the first night.

The motley group was herded into the barracks, filling the many rooms and hallways already clogged with prisoners. The evening wore long and lonely with no meal and little talk. All felt insecure and defenseless, surrounded by Senegalese with guns.

Ernst noticed one younger man singled out and taken away, then another. In time they returned.

The first one sat beside Ernst, trembling, but said nothing. He started to whimper. Ernst looked away to give the man privacy. Finally the man spoke in a shaky whisper to Ernst. "Do you know what that one over there did to me? He used me."

"He what? What do you mean?"

The man cursed, then added, "He raped me, that filthy . . ." He fell silent, dripping with shame. Suddenly the quietness was shattered by a man's scream . . . then another long scream from the same man, then another. A door opened and a German soldier stumbled into the room holding his hand over his mouth. His eyes stared a thousand yards into nothing. He sat down to avoid fainting and, removing his hand from his mouth, he spit a pool of fresh blood onto the floor.

"What happened? What did they do to you?" asked a prisoner who knew him.

"They ripped two teeth out of my mouth. . . ." He replied, swearing freely.

"What are you saying? Why?"

"The gold. They wanted the gold in my teeth."

He rolled up his shirt and clamped his jaws tight on it to stop the bleeding. The other men sat paralyzed as another was led out at gunpoint. A loud terrifying scream followed. He was returned as another was escorted out. This went on for some time.

Ernst tried to get comfortable on the floor. A large Senegalese guard lay down beside him and soon fell asleep, but Ernst stayed awake the entire night, traumatized by the lurking evil.

The next morning 300 hungry prisoners were marched thirty-five miles west to Nagold. Ernst's last meal had been the sandwich that had nearly stuck in his throat when the soldiers pounded on the door of his home the day before. His stomach made a growling demand as they passed a bakery, but the freedom to eat was gone.

The prisoners were put into a quarry and kept under the open sky for two days and nights. The gruff roar of diesel engines was heard the third day as trucks backed up to the quarry.

"Get on!" came the sharp command, and the men climbed onto the trucks. Destination? Knielingen, a town on the edge of Karlsruhe. The spring wind whipping through Ernst's hair felt free, but it was powerless to save him from sinking ever more deeply into hopelessness. He found himself envying the freedom of the cattle they passed in the fields.

"Get off!" came the next command when they arrived at Knielingen. As Ernst jumped down from the truck, he saw a huge door open wide, waiting to swallow them all. It was an unheated cement tank garage surrounded by a high fence laced with barbed wire. A loosely coiled strand of razor wire hung atop the fence. In front of the building was a fenced courtyard. Towers surrounded the compound, making escape impossible.

"Hey," barked a soldier looking directly into Ernst's eyes. "Take off those shoes!"

Ernst was glad that his good government-issued shoes were hidden as he unlaced his worn shoes and drew his feet out. He watched as the soldier tied the laces together and flung them over his shoulder. They were now his.

"Enter!" shouted a soldier. The cold cement floor was covered with straw. The grim walls were barely lit by five lightbulbs dangling from the ceiling. It was time for instructions.

"Take care of the straw because that's all you're going to get for a long time. There will be one meal a day—one piece of bread and some corn. That oil barrel in the middle of the floor is your toilet. Each morning two of you will empty it, so plan to take turns. You'll be fed tomorrow." Then the doors were slammed shut.

Disoriented, the men began talking quietly to one another. Nerves unraveled. "Get out of here or I'll kill you!" yelled one man as he fought with another over some straw. Ernst slumped to the floor in disbelief. Fresh air and freedom were gone, and now he was trapped in a building with men on the outer edge of sanity.

Hungry, depressed and confused, he curled up in some straw and fell asleep. He awoke hours later. The deep blackness was softened only by one dim light hanging in the center of the room. Ernst assumed it was the middle of the night. The stench of excrement filled his throat, and he felt the urge to wretch. He swallowed, but the pungent foulness remained. He opened his eyes to see a man sitting on the oil barrel relieving himself.

Many men had been to the barrel over the previous hours. The putrid air was mingled with cursing as the contents of the barrel spilled over, running under the straw of prisoners lying nearby. Pushing back, these men, in turn, crowded others. Threats were made.

Ernst locked his fingers behind his head and stared up into nothingness. Nostalgia took him by the arm and walked him deep into his past. Soon he was transported in sweet thought, forgetting for the moment the strangling odor of the building. He envisioned his mother laughing and singing. He smelled muffins baking over the fire. Then his thoughts shifted to his aunt and uncle's home: the love, the safety, the respect. He thought of lying in his bed with his pillow.

The scene changed. He was a little boy again. He felt the warm sun and cool breeze as he ran with Rico high up on the mountain behind his home. He could see forever from the mountain. Frolicking and running, he laughed. "Rico, come boy! C'mon, Rico, let's run some more," he called out in his hallucination.

Suddenly, there came a gruff, "Shut up, kid." Ernst was abruptly returned to reality. Hot tears ran down his cheeks. He bit his lip, trying to quiet the desperate longing of his soul.

Early the next morning the large doors were opened. Ernst could almost see the fresh air replace the stench. Two men carried the overflowing barrel to a dump. "Everybody outside," came the order. Three hundred men poured into the fenced courtyard where they received their meal: one piece of bread and one ear of field corn each. Not sweet corn, just hard field corn–the kind fed only to animals.

"Try to eat slowly, kid," said one prisoner to Ernst. "You'll feel like you're eating more that way. Snap the kernels off and chew them slowly. That way you'll shorten the gap between meals and your stomach won't ache as much later."

After they received a drink of water, the day slogged down into lying around and talking about nothing. Periodically the thought of the doors being shut again, enclosing the men around the barrel in the middle of the floor, caused Ernst to nearly vomit. But that would be his future, day after day, night after night.

Within a week, hunger felt like an animal trying to gnaw its way out of his body. The men's faces became gaunt. Some stepped beyond sanity and started babbling nonsense. Violent fights broke out over a scrap of food or a fistful of straw. Ernst watched men who were doctors, lawyers, and business owners, all acting equally crazed. His admiration for position and titles died.

Then one day the most unexpected thing happened, revealing a different side of humanity seen in only a few.

"My name is Robert Vatter," said a middle-aged prisoner, extending a hand of friendship.

"Is that so?" Ernst curtly replied. "Vatter is my name, too, though surely we're not related."

"No, probably not. I just want to ask you a question: Are you hungry?"

Ernst swore. "What kind of question is that? We're only getting one piece of bread and one ear of that lousy corn each day, and you ask if I'm hungry. Of course. I'm starving."

"Well, starting tomorrow I will give you one-half of my piece of bread. You are young and need it more than I do."

"How can you do that? Are you able to steal some?"

Robert pulled a thin Bible out of his pocket in his torn coat and said, "No, I will steal nothing. The Lord Jesus Christ will help me do it."

From the next day forward Ernst ate one and a half pieces of bread, plus an ear of corn. The impact of this unconditional, selfless love rammed against the wall surrounding his heart. But by that time the young man was so confused and embittered that the wall barely budged. As days passed and Robert stayed true to his word, Ernst thought, *If that's what a true Christian is, I wish I could be like that man.*

One day, while in the courtyard, a prisoner asked, "Ernst, do you know who occupies those tall buildings over there, the one where the windows are barred?"

"No."

"Some of the Nazi leaders who were in charge of villages and towns. They'll probably face execution," he said in a tone of cold reality that held no trace of regret.

Ernst looked at the windows and thought, *Just over there are men who caused me to be here. They tried to conquer the world with might and lost. Their strength cannot compare to Robert's: strength rooted in a Power within that makes him completely different.*

Several days later, there was a loud scuffle in the courtyard as soldiers wrestled a prisoner to the ground. An older man, whom Ernst recognized as being from his village, had walked too close to the fence, gesturing as though to climb over it. He may have been hallucinating, since he was too weak to escape anyway. Still, the soldiers took this opportunity to make a grand display of power. A decision was made to execute the man at 10 o'clock the next morning. The stench-filled garage was exceedingly quiet throughout the night.

At 10 o'clock sharp the prisoners were lined up and stripped to the waist to watch the slaying. Then the leader shouted at the blindfolded man to face the wall.

"Ready!" Six soldiers raised their rifles to their shoulders.

"Aim!" The six pressed their cheeks against their rifle stocks. Closing one eye, they squinted with the other, sighting the prisoner's heart in the cross hairs. The pause seemed eternal.

"Fire!" The prisoner dropped to the ground and lay motionless, though he was still breathing. No shots were heard.

Only six clicks. The guns weren't loaded. The commander then turned to the prisoners and warned sternly: "Let this be a lesson to all of you. This time I am showing mercy, but if any one of you tries to escape again, the guns will be loaded. You will be shot! Dismissed."

Ernst looked at the man lying on the ground, thinking that he had surely had a heart attack. To everyone's surprise, however, he had not–he had simply dropped from extreme fright.

Later, Ernst mustered the nerve to ask him, "Do you mind telling me what you thought about as you stood expecting to die?"

"My wife and children," replied the man. Then, following a long pause, he added, "Life, I thought about life."

There was no more commentary. Ernst didn't feel free to pursue the matter any further. But he realized that he, too, was beginning to think about that exact same thing–life. Arrested because of mistaken identity, he was in a place that stripped him of all self-respect and identity. He wondered who he was, what he was. His only touch with what it meant to be human was Robert. He clung to that thread of hope.

Still, the pendulum of threat didn't stop swinging above his head.

An excerpt from Ron Susek's encouraging and profound book of weekly meditations designed to challenge and encourage you to a deeper prayer life with God

God Will Answer

52 Meditations to Enrich Your Prayer Life

BY RON SUSEK

Baker Books
A Division of Baker Book House Co.
Grand Rapids, Michigan 49516

But If Not

He will rescue us from your hand, O king. But even if he does not,
we want you to know, O king, that we will not serve your gods.
Daniel 3:17-18

Faith empowers prayer, but what is faith? Is it merely a mustered-up feeling that forces God to act as you desire? Or is it the release of all rights to God, trusting him to answer according to his wisdom?

The latter was the view of the three Hebrew children Shadrach, Meshach, and Abednego. The story is well known, how they wouldn't bow to the image of gold established by the king of Babylon. The furnace of punishment was heated seven times greater than necessary to burn them alive. In fact, the king's men perished while adding fuel to the fire.

In human terms, this would have been a good time for the three Hebrew men to negotiate or even compromise. They could have bent their knee to the image, but not their hearts. Or they could have pacified this momentary whim of the king in order to stay alive and be future witnesses for Jehovah.

Nebuchadnezzar was white hot with rage to think of their insolence. He had favored them, lifting them from hard labor to serve in the palace. Still, they ignored his edict. *Impudent ingrates,* he must have thought. The fire in the furnace paled compared to his rage.

It's in this context that these young men made one of the greatest statements, a classic of all time: "If we are thrown into the blazing furnace, the God we serve is able to save us from it, and he will rescue us from your hand, O King. But even if he does not . . . we will not serve your gods or worship the image of gold you have set up" (Dan. 3:17-18).

Now that's faith! It took absolute trust in God to do what was right whether it meant deliverance or demise. Job said it this way: "Though he slay me, yet will I hope in him" (Job 13:15).

This kind of faith made three Hebrew men unstoppable. They wouldn't negotiate with unbelief. Their uncompromising faith forced pagans to face God head-on. There was no way around it. Their willingness to die for God compelled the world to consider Jehovah.

This faith also gave Jehovah options in how to reveal himself. In this case it was through deliverance. What was the result? This may have been the very event that jolted Nebuchadnezzar toward his eventual conversion. Beyond this it took seven years of insanity to prepare the pagan's heart, but he did eventually honor Jehovah: "Therefore I decree that the people of any nation or language who say anything against the God of Shadrach, Meshach and Abednego be cut into pieces and their houses be turned into piles of rubble, for no other god can save in this way" (Dan. 3:29).

Likewise, use very opportunity in your life to let God prove himself as he desires. Rather than consider the impact of consequences upon your personal situation, consider only how your faith may best honor God. Praying in faith that God will work wisely in your situation, stand firm on the ultimate expression of faith: *But if not . . . !*

Commune With God

Surely, Father, it was not an easy choice for the three Hebrew youths to honor you with such faith. Help me to mature to their level of faith and be able to so trust you amid threatening circumstances that I can say, "But if not, I still will not betray my God."

Make the Text Your Own

Day One: What key thought do you wish to remember from this meditation?

Day Two: According to Hebrews 11:1, what is faith? What biblical illustration helps you explain your definition of faith?

Day Three: What other examples in the Bible come to mind of those who acted upon God's faithfulness, character, and Word? What examples come to mind of Christ rebuking those who did not trust him?

Day Four: Read the "faith chapter" in Hebrews 11, then fill in the blank:
By faith _____ (your name)
believed God for _____, (act of God)
even though the present circumstances seem to prove otherwise.

Day Five: It's true that God loves you unconditionally and there's nothing you can do to make him love you more or love you any less. However, based upon a lack of faith or trust, you can displease him (see Heb. 11:6). Think of specific examples when loved ones didn't trust you or believe what you told them. How did you feel? How do you think God feels when you don't trust him?

An excerpt from Ron Susek's
best selling Biblical How-To book

Firestorm:

Preventing and Overcoming Church Conflicts

BY RON SUSEK

Baker Books
A Division of Baker Book House Co.
Grand Rapids, Michigan 49516

CHAPTER ONE

Phase 1—Sparks

Consider what a great forest is set on fire by a small spark.
James 3:5

Fires generally start from a small spark. Sparks of conflict between people are generated all the time and rarely go out. They can smolder often for years, in a deep emotional memory bank before erupting into a firestorm. To assume they will vanish is a grave mistake. So it was for Steve Gates and Central Baptist Church of Pittsburgh, Pennsylvania.

Steve graduated from seminary at age twenty-five, filled with quixotic fervor. Two weeks later he was a candidate for Central's senior pastor position. His talent and demeanor were about to sweep him past the maturing process of first holding associate positions and land him the top job at the outset. But ambition and ability cannot replace maturation under a mentor. No one on the pastoral search committee could have asked the right questions to unmask the impairments and hidden agendas beneath Steve's sparkling veneer. Only pressure and time could reveal such things—even to Steve himself.

Nor did Steve know all the right questions to ask the committee. Could he really succeed as a young pastor following

Dr. James Barnes, who had founded, then pastored the congregation of two hundred and forty for thirty-seven years? Was he developed enough to perceive the complexities of existing relationships? He gave no hint that anything was too big to handle.

Over the next three days of Steve's candidacy, he appeared to be a godsend. The church leaders said they wanted Central to grow, and Steve had the goods. His striking appearance enhanced his commanding elocution. He championed Baptist traditions. His snappy suits were a jump-start into the present from Dr. Barnes' tired, unpressed trousers. Yesss! . . . he'll even reach the youth. This thought quieted some older people who had doubts.

What about doctrine and theology? Very important! Steve scored high. Conservative views aligned. But there was another consideration . . . unmentioned, but vital–*culture*. While Steve dressed executive straight, there were unspoken differences in attitudes. Style of music, method of worship, manner of praying, and a thousand other unseen likes and dislikes lay hidden, ready to take on doctrinal ferocity if crossed. The church's culture formed a river of heartfelt familiarity, a sense of safety and identity, even establishing people's sense of well-being. Board members didn't catch Steve placating, rather than honoring, them with his answers. And Steve didn't perceive the importance of an established culture. He didn't realize how deeply personal preferences could be defended as divinely inspired. But everyone liked him. He knew it and assumed this meant they would be thrilled when the *real* Steve emerged–the explosively zealous young man with untested plans. He underestimated the "sacredness" of culture, as well as the strength of invisible power structures.

For instance, there was Ned Friendly, who held no office but had shared a close, mutually-significant friendship with Dr. Barnes. Serious church issues were discussed on the golf course, and Ned's fingerprints could be seen all over the outcome. Board member Bob Barkley was a willful, demanding, impetuous man in his mid-thirties. Being a salesman by day and a sports enthusiast by night, he thought all problems could be overcome with a good quarterback and a motivational slogan. Trustee Mark Mulrooney had taken over a large family business but still lived in the shadow of his eccentric father, whose ways drove Mark to obsession with correctness and conformity. While Mark didn't flaunt his wealth, it was known that his large tithes often delivered the church from shortfalls. And then there was Jim Bender, who was actually his wife's spokesman on the board. Unlike his wife, he lacked strong personal ideas and convictions. Everyone knew that what he said at one board meeting may change by the next, all depending on how his wife reacted at home.

Steve was unable to read these dynamics because he lacked the quiet, unobtrusive love with which a seasoned pastor slowly enters an established culture. He was assessing how the money people could help him fulfill his dreams. He was not aware that many wanted a Dr. Barnes reincarnated in Steve's youthful skin. Acceptance on both sides could only come by adjustments over time. The unanswered question was whether they would respect and reinforce each other until time made them one.

Cultures also have systemic problems, and CBC was no exception. Abusive power, even sin, lay deep in the structure. For instance, Bob Bulrich and Ivan Erikson had an unresolved dispute. Bob's son had romanced Ivan's daughter into engagement, then betrayed her for another. Ivan's daughter had started taking drugs, then had a child out of wedlock, all of which Ivan blamed on Bob's son. Ivan also resented Bob for acting as though his son had done no harm.

Bob, on the other hand, resented Ivan, thinking he should "act like a man" and just get over it. The old wound festered into bitterness, preventing the two families from agreeing on any church decision. Bob found sordid delight in knowing that he could flick the wound, causing it to thump anew, by opposing Ivan's ideas. Friends sided with each family, forming contentious power blocks.

Steve, too young to have been ripened on the vine and crushed in the winepress, was driven by impatient idealism, not weathered wisdom. More like Napolean than Paul, he didn't understand the timing of grace. Nor did he detect that the board was concealing existing problems with spiritual cosmetics, making the church sound like a preview of heaven. Steve was shown the rope of opportunity but not the hangman's noose at the end.

The weekend of Steve's candidacy drew to a close. It was time for the vote. Steve passed, at least for the present. He became Central Baptist's senior pastor. But already small sparks of disagreement had started a slow burn that eventually would explode into a full-blown firestorm.

The proverbial honeymoon began. Pastor Steve Gates and wife Heather were anxious to get started. They had two children, Michael, age three, and Michelle, eighteen months. Any lingering doubts within the congregation were diminished by Heather's warm, naïve personality and the laughter of two innocent children.

But it wasn't long before Steve bumped into resistance. Attitudes differed over church growth. While growth was desirable, the methods to be used and the changes it would bring caused division.

The first five years whisked by as Steve worked with tornadic force, always trying to compress two days' work into one. To him, the mandate was clear: The church said it wanted to grow, and he was the person to lead the charge. He was overflowing with ideas and dreams, all of which were fanned by attending numerous seminars on church growth. He launched efforts to increase membership–a bus ministry, concerts with Christian celebrities, well-known guest speakers, competition with attendance awards–all well-intended.

The silent resistance Steve encountered resulted from opposition to that one accursed word–*change*. Steve lowered his head like a linebacker and charged the opposition, accusing dissenters of lacking spiritual concern for the lost. In time, some viewed Steve as a threat to the way "God had led them" for thirty-seven years. Some familiar comfort zones were shrinking, pushed in by such occasions as the day Steve invited recording star Wanda Blondell to perform in a concert costing eighty-five hundred dollars. The church had to kick in three thousand dollars to pay her when ticket sales fell below expectations. Some on the board were angry that this never had been approved. Others argued that they must stand behind the pastor, since he was sent by God. Still another group didn't like the kind of people Wanda's upbeat music attracted. Younger people, though, wanted to smash the organ and have someone like Wanda every week. Steve secretly felt the foot-draggers were satanic plants. The church had never faced questions like, "Are we ready for change, or are we demanding conformity?" "Can we make concessions, or are we expecting compliance?" "Will we forfeit comfort, or cling to convenience?" Suddenly those questions were raised with a jolt.

Sparks that wouldn't die out started falling among the pews. Older men on the board wanted to harness and direct Steve's energies. He viewed them as trying to tie him down. Younger members of the board urged him on. Like Solomon's son Rehoboam, Steve deepened his resolve to lead the charge of the young rather than be a spiritual father to all ages.

The end of the first five years marked a pivotal moment. Attendance pushed five hundred. The church had to enlarge its facility or experience loss. Steve sat dreaming. Vision inspired vision. He envisioned not only a new auditorium with an educational wing but also foresaw a compound where missionaries could recuperate. He was intrigued by the idea of starting a seminary. He jotted down a generic name for it: Kingdom Seminary. Subconsciously he saw this as a way to assure his posterity, so he tore up that piece of paper and wrote another name: Gates Theological Seminary. He felt a flush of warmth at the thought of a life-size bronze of himself, raised before an ivy-draped stone archway. Popularity whispered into his ear that people would want this bronze, even though it was foreign to apostolic attitudes.

His second five years became a frenzy of new projects: radio broadcasts, television programs, and buildings. Numerical growth accelerated. When Steve returned from seminars with new ideas, they had to be instituted immediately. Unfortunately, no one was able to see the bad seeds being sown among the good.

Steve, like many young ministers, fastened his eyes on another spiritual leader, who was rising in prominence. He patterned his ministry after this man's success. He didn't sort the good from the bad but adopted everything just because it seemed to work. Steve focused on a model, not a mentor. The model was a heavy-handed leader who led by entrepreneurial dictate, not servant leadership–a serious flaw. But because attendance shot over a thousand, pragmatism ruled: If it worked, it must be right.

Despite the conflicts, the church was still in the early stage of experiencing occasional falling sparks, a happy time when people were relating to each other with goodwill, measured respect, humor, tolerance, and anticipation of more good things to come. As in all congregations, new problems always were emerging, but they never threatened the church as a whole.

There was an ongoing feud between Joan and Barbara, two choir members locked in fierce rivalry over solo opportunities. Then there was Fred the custodian, who threatened to quit if certain elders didn't stop parking on the grass by the entrance. Numerous complaints surfaced about the language Fred used when someone walked on a floor he had just polished.

Many people grappled with personal and family problems, often affecting relationships within the church. Sarah, for instance, who had been emotionally abused by a domineering father, had a distorted view of manhood and womanhood. She saw all men as power freaks and thought women had to fight for their rights.

Dave and Carol Goodman left the church because the services were too "professional and showy," conflicting with their simple Plymouth Brethren background. A small charismatic group pressed for a more experiential faith. Another group thought Steve was too conservative for the University of Pittsburgh intellectuals.

Financial growth brought its own problems. At budget time, cries for more funds came from every department. This led to serious staff tensions and committee conflicts. Henrietta Blander insisted that music was the key ingredient to church growth. Dwayne and Sylvia Ferndon argued that the music was too traditional and that the youth were the future of the church, so programs for them were where the big dollars should go. And so it was that each division thought its planet was the center of the universe.

Then came conflicts among the seven full-time staff members and three volunteers. Steve discovered that, while all the staffers he had hired agreed to their job descriptions, hidden agendas were tucked into their back pockets. Within three months, each was doing things the way he or she thought God's work should be done. Steve worked hard to keep the staff united in spirit and purpose. Then came the unexpected. He noticed some staffers were carving out chunks of church members as loyalists around themselves. These became political power blocks to be used as bargaining chips for achieving their desires. Resentment and distrust grew within the staff.

Still, these were only the normal sparks generated by a group of any size. Nothing was unmanageable. The church was moving forward. As years passed, Steve and the church won national acclaim. Denominational leaders pointed their fingers in his direction anytime they wanted to show other pastors "how to do it." But no one realized the complexity of difficulties that, at times, made Steve want to leave the ministry.

Slowly, the unthinkable took place. Steve became more absorbed with his goals than in meeting people's needs. He increasingly used his shepherd's staff as a club to drive rather than as a hook to guide. He spurned people for feeling hurt or misunderstood, leaving issues unresolved. To him, talking out problems was a sign of weakness. He raised a wall around himself, not permitting anyone to peer over and see his own flaws. While this appeared as strength to the imperceptive, Steve was violating a cardinal truth: The wall one builds around his heart to keep out future plain locks in present and past problems. The apostle Paul's teaching about finding Christ's strength in weakness made good preaching but didn't get applied to Steve's personal life.

With eyes fastened upon his model, Steve forged ahead. Growth became his benchmark for success. People grew uneasy about the mounting debt. When elders tried to talk to him about cutting back, he sharply chided them for their lack of faith. If anyone persisted with their concerns, he warned them not to "touch God's anointed." He gradually turned from a servant-minister to a demanding master. Still, no one could foresee this ascending rocket exploding in midair. Success gave the illusion of invincibility.

The board should have seen Steve's error, but no one discerned the signs. This was the time when the church should have fulfilled its role, one that even seminaries are not equipped to do–mature pastors. Seminaries can only provide the tools for personal and professional growth. But wisdom and maturity are products of the pressures and practice of pastoring. By not detecting and addressing Steve's improper motivation, the board ultimately failed the church. Herein, the board shared full responsibility for the coming firestorm.

As the church approached the end of the first decade with Steve, some elders believed he no longer was the same person who first came to the church. But he was. People and events were not making Steve what he was; they were unmasking what he was. One day elder Charles Bradley met with Steve in his office. "Pastor," he said, "some people who are feeling neglected have talked to me. Is there a chance you could do a little more visitation?" Steve sighed with disgust. Charles felt like a fool for mentioning the matter, although he knew he was right.

"Charles," Steve responded, "aren't you satisfied with my sermons?"

"Yes, of course. Everyone thinks you are a great expositor."

"And aren't you pleased with our growth and building programs?"

"Of course, of course, Pastor."

"Well, I can't be out running around to hospitals, nursing homes, and family picnics, while at the same time building this church." Steve stood silent, his closing statement made.

Charles walked away, feeling tongue-lashed by a cold, harsh spirit. He couldn't explain it, just felt it. He felt insignificant and powerless. As an elder, he should have some access to the pastor's heart. But the truth was painfully clear. He felt like a worthless pawn, not a co-servant. His spurned attempt to help Steve started a smoldering frustration in Charles's heart.

In this exchange, Steve was hiding behind his strength, rather than facing his weakness. He never analyzed himself deeply enough to realize that his aloofness was rooted in his lack of love for people. The thought of sitting with a mature saint in a nursing home almost suffocated him. His mind was churning with ideas on how to preach to a larger audience by adding more television stations. He was consumed by how to raise money to finance his plans. People? They'd have to understand and appreciate what they had in a pastor and stop wanting more.

Charles wasn't the only one to bump into Steve's resolve. Parishioners often left his office from counseling sessions feeling as though he had not really heard them. Sometimes, when people needed his help, he was either bent over a new set of blueprints or masterminding another promotional scheme. They had neither his interest nor his attention.

For instance, while Mary Sadler was unloading her burden to Steve about her son's disregard for authority, Steve grabbed a pen and wrote a note. She was pleased to think that he was that interested in her problem. Steve dismissed himself, claiming to need some water. He went to the outer office and whispered to his secretary, Paula Harth, to set up an appointment with the contractor for the retirement village. While he was out, Mary looked at the note, curious to know what she had said that was so important. She read, "Get final blueprint draft from Paul Craft." Disappointment surged through her. She was visibly shaken when Steve returned, and abruptly excused herself and left. She felt mugged, violated, cheated. She told no one of her hurt, but unknowingly joined a long list of people who would not stand behind Steve in the hour of fiery trial.

Steve thought that people should simply get over whatever bothered them and move on to the bigger picture. He forgot that in God's heart people *are* the picture. He lost sight of Jesus' priorities. Steve's focus was on crowds, not individuals–a motivation agitated by the lure of celebrity status, a cancer of our media age. He forgot that the only mantle of greatness is to carry a towel of service (John 13:13-17).

Spiritually-minded people grew uneasy. They sensed trouble was on the horizon but couldn't define it. Edna Neel and other intercessors felt led to pray, often finding themselves disturbed in the middle of the night. Only God could know how many sparks of unrest flickered in people's hearts.

Let's analyze what is happening in this initial phase. Firestorms ignite from various sparks:

- Someone has an unthreatening complaint about the pastor or board.
- A group is in conflict over a procedural issue.
- Some feel the board is acting unfairly on a problem.
- A group is unhappy about a certain direction the church is taking.
- Someone feels slighted or insulted.
- A pastor may be abusing his position.

The unhappy people generally lack the clout, desire, or fortitude to set a firestorm into motion, so they use small power plays to express their grievance:

- They quit the choir.

- They stop giving.
- They complain to family and friends.
- They formally complain to the board.
- They leave the church.

If enough people suffer injustice (perceived or real), in time a firestorm will erupt.

Most people who raise issues in phase one intend good, not harm, for the church. They simply want to vent and resolve their grievances, after which they will resume normal participation. If they are not satisfied, they may withdraw from involvement. Above all, they are not troublemakers.

The Natural Dynamics of Phase 1

Natural dynamics of human relationships on this level:

1. Real, God-given differences exist in people, such as:

- Goals: What people want to see happen for themselves, their families, and the church.
- Needs: What people require for their children, personal growth, cultural traditions, and religious experience.
- Perspectives: Everyone views issues from a different set of experiences and will naturally approach problems from these various points of view.
- Values: People's codes of right and wrong, worth and worthlessness are determined from a wide range of views, from biblical absolutes to humanistic relativism.
- Methods: How people believe things should be done–how to organize, lead and have authority roles.
- Interests: Myriad personal preferences, such as style of worship, type of music, architecture.

We must be very clear at this point that these differences generally are not sinful or evil but God-given. These legitimate differences must be respected and honored, as well as blended (which is basic in spiritual growth), otherwise they will produce a long series of sparks that can ignite a firestorm. On this level, people can still be led to respond to their differences through the following:

- Acceptance (I choose to want you.)
- Adjustment (I choose to change for you.)
- Appreciation (I choose to understand you.)

People are not competing in their differences on this level; rather, they are tolerant and even enjoy their differences. When this normal interaction moves into conflict, harmless differences become emotional focal points. Not all firestorms start with malicious intent, just a lack of maturity in handling these differences. If leadership fails here, people's dispositions will change from collaborative to adversarial.

While leadership ministers, it is God alone who molds. When people's distinctiveness is ignored and an attempt is made to conform everyone to the leadership's image, small fires ignite. Peter wrote of proper leadership, "Not lording it over those entrusted to you, but being examples to the flock" (1 Peter 5:3). True pastoral leadership nurtures the best in people, even if the people's various perspectives cause the pastor's path for the church to meander like a stream in directions that don't fit his straight-line goals. A pastor must be primarily given to the people's good and not his own inflexible goals.

This is not to suggest that the church is run by a disjointed collection of opinions. That would be as ridiculous as a football team on which each man ran in any direction he desired. Randomness is anarchy when applied to human behavior. The Scriptures enjoin people to honor leadership (1 Thess. 5:12-13). Still, leadership is God-given to direct, not dominate.

When leadership dominates, people feel they are doing the leaders' ministry and not being equipped to do their own ministry, resulting in either anger or ambivalence. A pastor is not directed to get people to do the pastor's ministry but to equip believers to fulfill their ministries (Eph. 4:11-12). When the minister equips people instead of using them to accomplish his own agenda, they generally gain a sense of ownership that makes them highly productive.

2. During this phase, when problems emerge, most people are still focused on issues. They are not attacking each other. There is keen interest in solving a mutual problem.

3. People use respectful, considerate, noncondemning language.

4. In a desire to solve the problem, both sides are not threatened by sharing information and ideas. They are not protecting their positions. Suspicion has not set in.

5. People remain rational in problem-solving. Resolution comes either through informal, personal settlements or in formal ways, such as voting. There is not a sense of mortal loss if one's position doesn't win.

6. People are focused on a resolution that can give everyone a sense of winning because the cause of Christ benefits. Every effort is made to have each person's ideas and contribution be part of the solution. If someone's perspective is bypassed, the greatest care is taken to make the person understand why it would not have worked well at this point. But the person is still made to feel appreciated and needed–not devalued.

Recommendations for Phase 1

• Never allow church growth to shift the emphasis away from the value of the individual. Discipling people does not mean to nurture them until they are mature enough to be ignored. Relationship is central to God's plan. It is generally considered that when a significant percentage of the congregation (10 to 15 percent, according to experts), feels used for the "cause," rather than valued and honored as a worthy part of the cause, then phase two is at the doorstep.

- Hold special meetings twice a year–one with an emphasis for believers, and the other for evangelism. Using the gifts given for equipping the body is crucial (Eph. 4:11-16).
- "Discovering the Real You" is a video series available through SEA that can be helpful in resolving conflict.
- Hold periodic leadership retreats, not for business but for spiritual and relationship development.
- Periodically study the biblical purpose and function of the board. Spiritual leadership and business leadership are different functions.
- Promptly respond to complaints and concerns with fairness and justice. Small offenses and misunderstandings rarely go away on their own.
- Conduct an exit interview to find out why people are leaving your church. They may give clues of a coming firestorm.
- At least once a year, take the board and church through the approved master plan. Never assume people are on track without keeping the plan before them. If they lose ownership of the master plan, it has already ceased to be a master plan and is reduced to the pastor's personal plan. Distrust develops if the leader gets too far out in front.
- Keep the staff clear in direction and united in spirit. Personal hidden agendas among staff are among the greatest causes of conflict.